Step-Up Workbook 2

Name: ....

Class: ....

NEW MATHS FRAMEWORKING

Jeanette Mumford
Simon and Helen Greaves

Contents

NUMBER AND ALGEBRA
1.1 Place value in numbers

● I can read and write numbers numbers to 100.

Numbers from 10 to 99 have two digits. The first digit shows the number of **tens**. The second digit shows the number of **units** (or ones).

73

Seventy-three
has **7 tens**
and **3 units**

98

Ninety-eight
has **9 tens**
and **8 units**

16

Sixteen
has **1 ten**
and **6 units**

1 Here are some numbers written in words. Write each number in figures.

a Sixty-two   62   b Twenty-seven

c Seventy-one   d Eighty-four

e Ninety-nine   f Forty-eight

g Thirty-three   h Nineteen

i Fifty-six   j Ninety-nine

2 Here are some numbers written in figures. Write each number in words.

a 47   forty-seven   b 68

c 77   d 29

e 80 [   ]   f 92 [   ]

g 13 [   ]   h 35 [   ]

i 51 [   ]   j 46 [   ]

3 Each of these things has a number on it.

23   80   62   39   85   90

a   How many units are there in the number on the red shoe?   [3] units

b   How many tens are there in the number on the orange shirt?   [ ] tens

c   How many units are there in the number on the brown trousers?   [ ] units

d   How many tens are there in the number on the red shoe?   [ ] tens

e   How many units are there in the number on the green shirt?   [ ] units

f   Which two things have the same number of tens?

[   ] and [   ]

◆ I can read and write numbers to 100.   [ ]

Let's try this!

Use the digits 4, 3, 8 and 1 to make as many different two digit numbers as you can. Write each number in figures and words.

4   3   8   1

1.2 Ordering numbers

I can order numbers to 100.

Key words
higher, lower, order, smaller, larger

Here are two numbers.   **72   24**

The number with the higher tens digit is the larger number, so 72 is the larger number.

Here are two more numbers.   **82   87**

The tens digit is the same for both numbers. Now look at the units digits.

The number with the higher units digit is the larger number, so 87 is the larger number.

1 Circle the smaller of the two numbers.

a (34) 78

b 65 54

c 97 94

d 35 53

e 50 48

f 22 21

2 Here are some numbers. For each set, write the largest number.

a 45 34 66 51 [66]

b 89 67 70 54 [ ]

c

34 78 72 66 ☐

d

65 34 43 61 ☐

e

53 43 49 57 ☐

f

90 89 99 91 ☐

3 Look at these cards.
Put the numbers in order from **smallest** to **largest**.

a

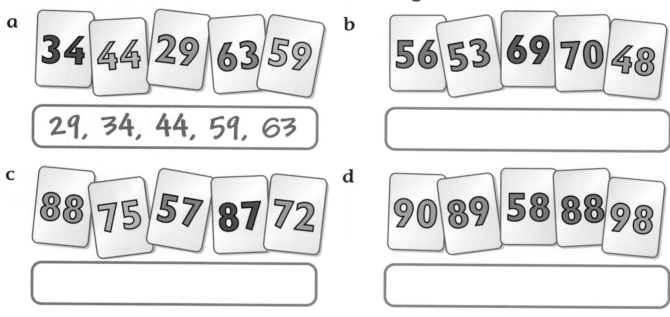

34 44 29 63 59

29, 34, 44, 59, 63

b

56 53 69 70 48

☐

c

88 75 57 87 72

☐

d

90 89 58 88 98

☐

◆ I can order numbers to 100. ☐

Let's try this!

Roll the two dice and write down a two-digit number they make.
Roll the two dice four more times and write down four more two-digit numbers.
Write your five numbers in order from the largest to the smallest.

1.3 Odd and even numbers

● I know about odd and even numbers.

Key words
odd, even, sequence

All numbers are either odd or even.

Odd numbers end in

or 9

Even numbers end in

or 8

The number 78 is even because it ends with 8.
The number 51 is odd because it ends with 1.

1 Look at these number cards.

a Put a tick under each **odd** number.

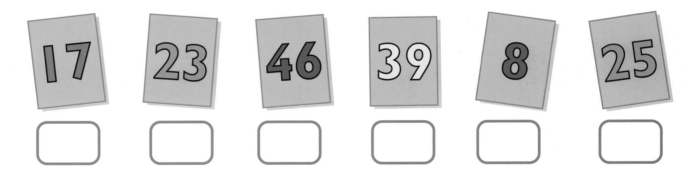

b Put a tick under each **even** number.

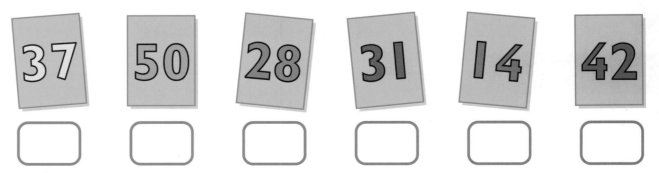

2 The numbers on the pickles in each jar are odd and even.

a Make a list of all the **odd** numbers in the jar.

b Make a list of all the **even** numbers in the jar.

3 Odd and even numbers can make **sequences**. A sequence is a pattern of numbers. Finish each sequence and say whether the numbers are odd or even.

a

b

c

d

I can know about odd and even numbers.

Let's try this!

Get a pack of number cards from 0–9.

Pick any two cards to make a number.

Say whether the number is odd or even.

Now do this four times using two different cards each time.

Remember to say whether the number is odd or even.

● I can count in twos, fives and tens.

Key words
count, sequence

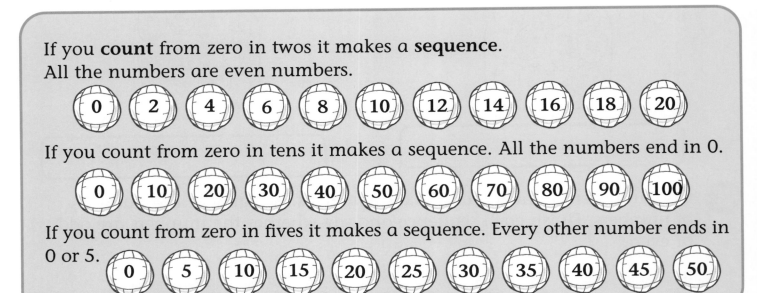

If you **count** from zero in twos it makes a **sequence**.
All the numbers are even numbers.

0 2 4 6 8 10 12 14 16 18 20

If you count from zero in tens it makes a sequence. All the numbers end in 0.

0 10 20 30 40 50 60 70 80 90 100

If you count from zero in fives it makes a sequence. Every other number ends in 0 or 5.

0 5 10 15 20 25 30 35 40 45 50

1 Finish the number sequences by counting on in twos, fives or tens.

a   8, 10, 12, 14, 16 , 18 , 20 , 22 , 24 , 26

b   30, 40, 50, 60, ☐ , ☐ , ☐ , ☐ , ☐ , ☐

c   15, 20, 25, 30, ☐ , ☐ , ☐ , ☐ , ☐ , ☐

d   20, 22, 24, 26, ☐ , ☐ , ☐ , ☐ , ☐ , ☐

e   80, 90, 100, 110, ☐ , ☐ , ☐ , ☐ , ☐ , ☐

f   45, 50, 55, 60, ☐ , ☐ , ☐ , ☐ , ☐ , ☐

2 In each bag there is one ball that does not belong there.
Write the number of the ball that does not belong in each bag.

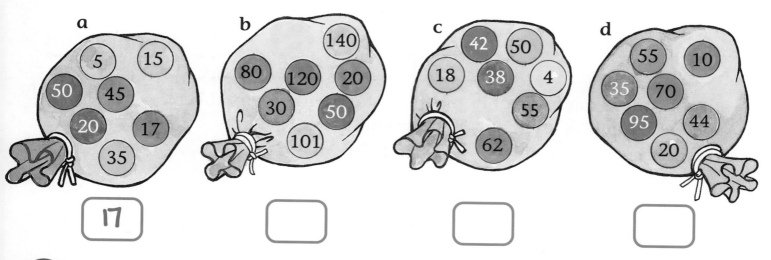

a   17

b   [ ]

c   [ ]

d   [ ]

3 Write in the missing numbers in each sequence.

a   150, 140, 130, **120** , **110** , 100, **90** , **80** , **70**

b   50, 45, 40, [ ] , [ ] , [ ] , 20, [ ] , [ ]

c   38, 36, 34, [ ] , [ ] , [ ] , [ ] , [ ] , 22

d   1, 3, [ ] , 7, [ ] , [ ] , [ ] , [ ] , [ ] , 19

e   175, 170, 165, [ ] , [ ] , 150, [ ] , [ ] , 135

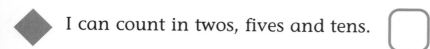 I can count in twos, fives and tens. [ ]

Let's try this!

Write down the number 70.
Count on from 70 in twos until you have ten numbers in
your sequence.
Start again at 70. This time, count back in twos until you
have ten numbers in your sequence.
Try this again – this time count on, then back, in fives.

More sequences

● I can make a sequence of numbers using a rule.

Key words
sequence, rule

A **sequence** is a pattern of numbers. It starts with one number.
The next numbers are found by following a **rule**.
This sequence starts with the number 4. The rule is **add 3**.

+3   7   10   13   16   19   22   25   28   31

1 Use the rule to complete each sequence of numbers.

a   +4   3   7   11 | 15 | | 19 | | 23 |

b   +5   1   6   11   ☐ ☐ ☐

c   −10   73   63   53   ☐ ☐ ☐

d   −3   24   21   18   ☐ ☐ ☐

2 Finish each number sequence using the rule.

a   Add 5   6, 11, 16, 21, ☐, ☐, ☐, ☐

b   Add 4   2, 6, 10, 14, ☐, ☐, ☐, ☐

c Subtract 2   40, 38, 36, 34, ☐ , ☐ , ☐ , ☐

d Subtract 10   98, 88, 78, 68, ☐ , ☐ , ☐ , ☐

3 Use the rule in each block to fill in the missing numbers in each sequence.

a +4 4, 8, 12, 16 , 20, 24 , 28 , 32

b +5 4, 9, ☐ , 19, ☐ , ☐ , ☐

c +3 8, 11, ☐ , ☐ , ☐ , 23, ☐

d −5 65, 60, 55, ☐ , ☐ , ☐ , ☐

e −4 36, ☐ , ☐ , ☐ , ☐ , ☐ , ☐

f −3 50, 47, ☐ , ☐ , ☐ , ☐ , ☐

g +2 7, ☐ , 11, ☐ , ☐ , ☐ , ☐

◆ I can make a sequence of numbers using a rule.   ☐

Let's try this!

Pick one card from the top row. This will be the first number in your sequence. Pick one card from the bottom row. Use this rule to continue your sequence until you have six numbers in your sequence.

Choose two different cards and try again.

22 25 31 40 42

+3 −2 +5 +10 −4

ADDITION AND SUBTRACTION

2.1 Addition and subtraction facts for 100 and 200

● I know addition and subtraction facts for 100 and 200.

Key words
addition,
subtraction

You have already added pairs of numbers to make 10 and 20.
Now you can add pairs of numbers to make 100 and 200.

$$3 + 7 = 10$$
$$30 + 70 = 100$$

$$12 + 8 = 20$$
$$120 + 80 = 200$$

You have already subtracted numbers from 10 and 20.
Now you can subtract numbers from 100 and 200.

$$10 - 4 = 6$$
$$100 - 40 = 60$$

$$20 - 5 = 15$$
$$200 - 50 = 150$$

1 Use the given addition or subtraction facts to complete the calculation below them.

a $4 + 6 = 10$

$\boxed{40} + \boxed{60} = \boxed{100}$

d $10 - 3 = 7$

$\boxed{} - 30 = \boxed{}$

b $9 + 1 = 10$

$\boxed{} + \boxed{} = 100$

e $10 - 4 = 6$

$100 - \boxed{} = \boxed{}$

c $5 + 5 = 10$

$50 + \boxed{} = \boxed{}$

f $10 - 8 = 2$

$\boxed{} - 80 = \boxed{}$

2 Draw lines to join similar pairs of addition and subtraction facts.

a   11 + 9 = 20   130 + 70 = 200

b   20 – 4 = 16   110 + 90 = 200

c   15 + 5 = 20   200 – 40 = 160

d   20 – 5 = 15   200 – 120 = 80

e   13 + 7 = 20   150 + 50 = 200

f   20 – 12 = 8   200 – 50 = 150

3 Complete these addition and subtraction facts.

a   30 + ☐ = 100   b   100 – 40 = ☐

c   200 – 70 = ☐   d   120 + ☐ = 200

e   200 – 160 = ☐   f   50 + ☐ = 200

 I know addition and subtraction facts for 100 and 200. ☐

Let's try this!

Find **three** strawberries that **add** together to make 100.

How many ways can you find to do this?

Now try to find three strawberries that add together to make 200.

2.2 Subtraction using addition

● I can use addition facts to work out subtraction facts.

Key words
add, subtract

You can use an addition fact to work out a subtraction fact.

6 + 8 = 14   so   14 – 8 = 6   21 + 8 = 29   so   29 – 8 = 21
                 and   14 – 6 = 8   and   29 – 21 = 8

1 Use the addition fact to write two different subtraction facts.

a   8 + 7 = 15 $\boxed{15} - \boxed{7} = \boxed{8}$ $\boxed{15} - \boxed{8} = \boxed{7}$

b   5 + 9 = 14 $\boxed{} - \boxed{} = \boxed{}$ $\boxed{} - \boxed{} = \boxed{}$

c   12 + 8 = 20 $\boxed{} - \boxed{} = \boxed{}$ $\boxed{} - \boxed{} = \boxed{}$

d   35 + 4 = 39 $\boxed{} - \boxed{} = \boxed{}$ $\boxed{} - \boxed{} = \boxed{}$

e   18 + 5 = 23 $\boxed{} - \boxed{} = \boxed{}$ $\boxed{} - \boxed{} = \boxed{}$

f   40 + 9 = 49 $\boxed{} - \boxed{} = \boxed{}$ $\boxed{} - \boxed{} = \boxed{}$

2 You can work out the missing number in a subtraction by turning it into an addition sum.

a [ ] − 4 = 6

Turn this into the addition

6 + 4 = 10

The missing number is [10].

b [ ] − 5 = 3

Turn this into the addition

3 + 5 = [ ]

The missing number is [ ].

c [ ] − 9 = 11

Turn this into the addition

[ ] + [ ] = [ ]

The missing number is [ ].

d [ ] − 14 = 5

Turn this into the addition

[ ] + [ ] = [ ]

The missing number is [ ].

3 Use the subtraction fact to write the addition fact.

a 14 − 5 = 9   [9] + [5] = [14]

b 12 − 8 = 4   [ ] + [ ] = [ ]

c 20 − 14 = 6   [ ] + [ ] = [ ]

◆ I can use addition facts to work out subtraction facts. [ ]

Let's try this!

Choose two items from the treasure chest.
Write an addition fact using the two numbers.
Now write two different subtraction facts for your addition fact.

8 + 4 = 12
12 − 4 = 8
and
12 − 8 = 4

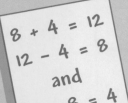

● I can add tens to and subtract tens from a number.

Key words
add, subtract, tens

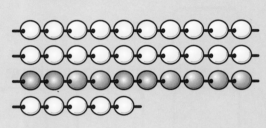

Here are 25 beads laid out as two sets of 10 beads and five single beads.

To add 10 beads …
25 + 10 = 35
The units digit stays the same and the tens digit goes up by one – from 2 to 3.
This is because you have added 10.

To add 20 beads …
25 + 20 = 45
The units digit stays the same and the tens digit goes up by two – from 2 to 4. This is because you have added two sets of 10.

1 Complete these additions.

a   28 + 10 = 38   b   35 + 10 =   c   12 + 20 =

d   35 + 20 =   e   16 + 30 =   f   42 + 30 =

g   29 + 40 =   h   13 + 50 =   i   17 + 10 =

j   38 + 30 =   k   27 + 20 =   l   18 + 50 =

2 When you subtract 10 from a number, the tens digit goes down by 1. Complete these subtractions.

a   27 – 10 = $\boxed{17}$ b   36 – 10 = ☐   c   49 – 10 = ☐

d   22 – 10 = ☐   e   58 – 10 = ☐   f   71 – 10 = ☐

3 Now do these additions and subtractions.

a   25 + 10 = $\boxed{35}$ b   34 – 10 = ☐   c   47 + 20 = ☐

d   48 – 20 = ☐   e   65 + 30 = ☐   f   78 – 40 = ☐

g   22 + 60 = ☐   h   84 – 50 = ☐   i   17 + 60 = ☐

j   48 – 30 = ☐   k   96 – 50 = ☐   l   28 + 20 = ☐

m   65 – 20 = ☐   n   44 + 30 = ☐   o   35 + 50 = ☐

p   92 – 10 = ☐

◆ I can add tens to and subtract tens from a number. ☐

Let's try this!

Choose one of these cards…   Now choose one of these cards…

Write out and complete the addition or subtraction.
Do this four times with different cards.

Adding two two-digit numbers

• I can add two two-digit numbers together.

Key words
add, digits, tens, units

Here is a way to add together two two-digit numbers.

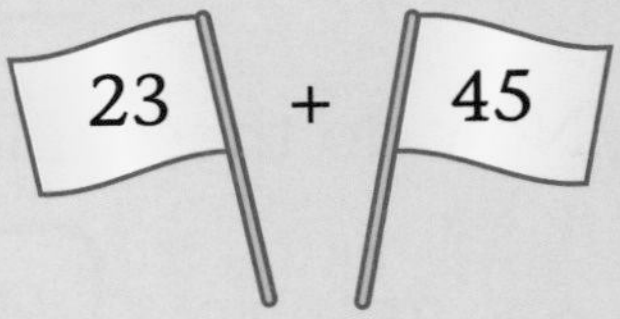

23 + 45

Split the second number into tens and units

$23 + 40 + 5$

Add the tens number on first

$63 + 5$

Now add on the units

68

1 **a** 24 + 15

= 24 + 10 + 5

= 34 + 5

= 39

b 32 + 44

= 32 + 40 + 4

= 72 + ☐

= ☐

c 61 + 37

= 61 + 30 + 7

= ☐ + ☐

= ☐

d 53 + 36

= 53 + ☐ + ☐

= ☐ + ☐

= ☐

2 Use the way you added on page 20. Write what you did in the box.
Circle the right answer.

a 26 + 32 | 26 + 30 + 2 = 56 + 2 | 60   (58)   52   26

b 34 + 51 | | 88   75   85   58

c 44 + 25 | | 66   79   96   69

d 63 + 15 | | 78   87   88   68

3 Add together each pair of numbers on the flags.
Show your working in the box.

a 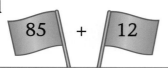   26 + 13
| 26 + 10 + 3 = 36 + 3 = 39 |

b    47 + 22

c 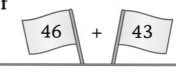   62 + 37

d   85 + 12

e   26 + 42

f   46 + 43

 I can add two two-digit numbers together. ☐

Let's try this!

Choose one blue number and one yellow number.
Add the two numbers together.
Try this for as many different pairs of numbers as you can.

34   22   14   41   12   51   23   35

2.5 Subtracting two two-digit numbers

● I can subtract a two-digit number from another two-digit number.

Key words
subtract, digit, tens, units

Here is a way to subtract one two-digit number from another:

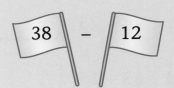

Split the second number into tens and units   38 – 10 – 2

Subtract the tens number first   28 – 2

Now subtract the units   **26**

1   **a**   24 – 13

= [24] – [10] – [3]

= [14] – [3]

= [11]

b   38 – 25

= [38] – [20] – [5]

= [18] – [   ]

= [   ]

c   69 – 37

= [69] – [30] – [7]

= [   ] – [   ]

= [   ]

d   55 – 34

= [55] – [   ] – [   ]

= [   ] – [   ]

= [   ]

2 Use the way you subtracted on page 22. Write what you did in the box. Circle the right answer.

a 34 − 13 | 34 − 10 − 3 = 24 − 3 = 21 | 20   (21)   23   11

b 58 − 26 | | 30   42   32   34

c 79 − 35 | | 44   54   34   46

d 94 − 41 | | 35   50   43   53

3 Subtract the numbers. Make sure you subtract the smaller number from the larger number.

a

62 − 50 − 1 = 12 − 1 = 11

b

c

d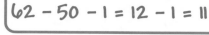

e

f

 I can subtract a two-digit number from another two-digit number.

Let's try this!

Choose one red number and one green number. Subtract the green number from the red number. Write down your answer. Try this for as many different pairs of numbers as you can.

 86   78   15   25

69   57   34   43

TIMES TABLES

3.1 Two and ten times tables

● I know the two and ten times tables.

Key words
multiplication, times tables

Multiplication is all about finding several sets of a number.

So 5 sets of 2 paper clips make 10.

Or 5 multiplied by 2 is 10.

We also write this as $5 \times 2 = 10$

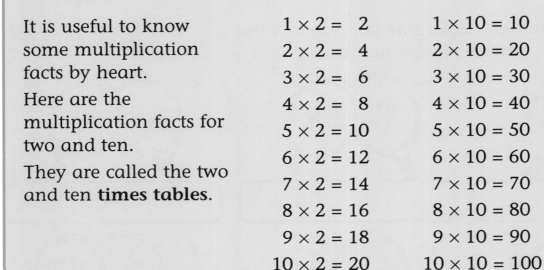

It is useful to know some multiplication facts by heart.

Here are the multiplication facts for two and ten.

They are called the two and ten **times tables**.

$1 \times 2 = 2$	$1 \times 10 = 10$
$2 \times 2 = 4$	$2 \times 10 = 20$
$3 \times 2 = 6$	$3 \times 10 = 30$
$4 \times 2 = 8$	$4 \times 10 = 40$
$5 \times 2 = 10$	$5 \times 10 = 50$
$6 \times 2 = 12$	$6 \times 10 = 60$
$7 \times 2 = 14$	$7 \times 10 = 70$
$8 \times 2 = 16$	$8 \times 10 = 80$
$9 \times 2 = 18$	$9 \times 10 = 90$
$10 \times 2 = 20$	$10 \times 10 = 100$

1 Write the missing numbers for these two times table facts.

a $2 \times 2 =$ **4**

b $4 \times 2 =$ ☐

c $8 \times 2 =$ ☐

d   ☐ $\times 2 = 10$

e   ☐ $\times 2 = 20$

f   ☐ $\times 2 = 14$

g $3 \times 2 =$ ☐

h   ☐ $\times 2 = 18$

2 Write the ten times table fact to show the total number of pencils in the boxes.

a   2   ×   10   =   20

b   ☐   ×   10   =   ☐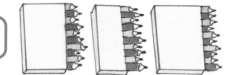

c   ☐   ×   ☐   =   ☐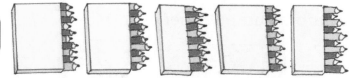

d   ☐   ×   ☐   =   ☐

3 Draw lines to join each multiplication to its answer.

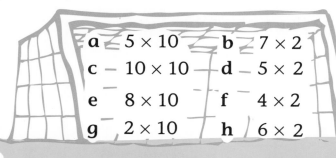

a	5 × 10	**b**	7 × 2
c	10 × 10	**d**	5 × 2
e	8 × 10	**f**	4 × 2
g	2 × 10	**h**	6 × 2

8   80   10   20   50

 14   12   100

◆ I know the two and ten times tables.   ☐

Let's try this!

Draw pictures of two and ten times tables facts.
Here is a picture to show the fact:
10 × 2 = 20

● I know the five times table.

Key words
multiplication, times tables

Here are the multiplication facts for five.
This is called the five **times table**.

You can see that all the answers to the fives
times table end in either 5 or 0.

$1 \times 5 = 5$
$2 \times 5 = 10$
$3 \times 5 = 15$
$4 \times 5 = 20$
$5 \times 5 = 25$
$6 \times 5 = 30$
$7 \times 5 = 35$
$8 \times 5 = 40$
$9 \times 5 = 45$
$10 \times 5 = 50$

1 Write in the missing numbers for the five times table facts.

a $2 \times 5 = \boxed{10}$

b $4 \times 5 = \boxed{}$

c $9 \times 5 = \boxed{}$

d $\boxed{} \times 5 = 15$

e $\boxed{} \times 5 = 50$

f $\boxed{} \times 5 = 35$

g $\boxed{} \times 5 = 40$

h $\boxed{} \times 5 = 25$

i $6 \times 5 = \boxed{}$

j $\boxed{} \times 5 = 5$

2 Multiply the numbers on the fruit by 5.

a [8] × [5] = [40]

b [ ] × [ ] = [ ]

c [ ] × [ ] = [ ]

d [ ] × [ ] = [ ]

3 Circle the multiplication fact that matches the number in the star.

a ☆25   2 × 5   4 × 5   7 × 5   (5 × 5)

b ☆50   3 × 5   10 × 5   8 × 5   1 × 5

c ☆15   6 × 5   9 × 5   3 × 5   2 × 5

d ☆40   7 × 5   8 × 5   6 × 5   9 × 5

e ☆35   3 × 5   7 × 5   5 × 5   4 × 5

◆ I know the five times table. [ ]

Let's try this!

Choose one of the five times table facts.
Draw a picture of one five times table fact.

Here is a picture of six rows of five pears to show the fact: 6 × 5 = 30

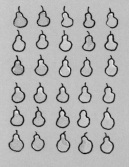

Three and four times tables

● I know the three and four times tables.

Here are the multiplication facts for three – the three times table:

$1 \times 3 = 3$

$2 \times 3 = 6$

$3 \times 3 = 9$

$4 \times 3 = 12$

$5 \times 3 = 15$

$6 \times 3 = 18$

$7 \times 3 = 21$

$8 \times 3 = 24$

$9 \times 3 = 27$

$10 \times 3 = 30$

1 Now work out this four times table.

$1 \times 4 = 4$

$\boxed{2} \times 4 = \boxed{8}$

$\boxed{} \times 4 = \boxed{}$

$\boxed{} \times 4 = \boxed{}$

$\boxed{} \times 4 = \boxed{}$

$\boxed{} \times 4 = \boxed{}$

$\boxed{} \times 4 = \boxed{}$

$\boxed{} \times 4 = \boxed{}$

$\boxed{} \times 4 = \boxed{}$

2 Write the missing numbers to complete these multiplication facts from the three and four times tables.

a 3 × 3 = ☐

b 5 × 4 = ☐

c 10 × 3 = ☐

d 6 × 4 = ☐

e ☐ × 3 = 15

f ☐ × 4 = 32

g ☐ × 3 = 21

h ☐ × 4 = 28

3 Each number that goes into the machine is multiplied by either 3 or 4. Write the missing numbers that come out of each machine.

a

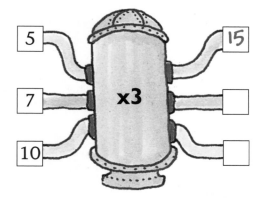

b

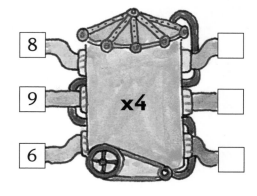

 I know three and four times tables. ☐

Let's try this!

Look again at pages 24-29 about the 2, 3, 4, 5 and 10 times tables.
Write some multiplication facts that have the same answer.

2 × 2 = 4

1 × 4 = 4

Dividing by two, five and ten

● I can use my times tables to divide numbers by two, five and ten.

Key words
multiply, divide, total

Division is the opposite of multiplication.

You can use the multiplication facts from the times tables to work out some division facts.

Here are ten pairs of shoes.

To work out the total number of shoes you can multiply 10 by 2.

We write this as $10 \times 2 = 20$

If you share the 20 shoes into sets of two, you get 10 pairs.

Or you can say 20 divided by 2 is 10.

We write this as $20 \div 2 = 10$

$10 \times 2 = 20$ so $20 \div 2 = 10$

1 Use the multiplication facts to make division facts.

a	$4 \times 2 = 8$	so	8	÷	2	= 4
b	$6 \times 2 = 12$	so	12	÷	2	= ☐
c	$5 \times 2 = 10$	so	10	÷ ☐		= ☐
d	$8 \times 2 = 16$	so	☐	÷	2	= ☐
e	$9 \times 2 = 18$	so	☐	÷ ☐		= ☐
f	$7 \times 2 = 14$	so	☐	÷ ☐		= ☐
g	$10 \times 2 = 20$	so	☐	÷ ☐		= ☐
h	$3 \times 2 = 6$	so	☐	÷ ☐		= ☐

2 Draw lines to join each multiplication fact with its division fact.

a $5 \times 10 = 50$ $70 \div 10 = 7$

b $4 \times 10 = 40$ $50 \div 10 = 5$

c $9 \times 10 = 90$ $40 \div 10 = 4$

d $7 \times 10 = 70$ $90 \div 10 = 9$

3 There are five cakes in each row.
Use the picture to complete the division facts.

a $10 \div 5 = \boxed{}$ b $20 \div 5 = \boxed{}$

c $25 \div 5 = \boxed{}$ d $30 \div 5 = \boxed{}$

◆ I can use my times tables to divide numbers by two, five and ten. $\boxed{}$

Let's try this!

Choose a number from 1 to 10 and then choose one number from 2, 5 and 10.

Write the multiplication fact that uses both of these numbers.

Then write the division fact that goes with it.

Do this for as many pairs of numbers as you can.

Multiplication fact
$6 \times 5 = 30$
Division fact
$30 \div 5 = 6$

3.5 Dividing by three and four

● I can use my times tables to divide numbers by three and four.

Key words
multiply, divide

Here are three rows of balloons. Each row has four balloons.
To find the total number of balloons, multiply three by four.

$3 \times 4 = 12$

There are 12 balloons altogether.

To find the number of balloons in each row, divide twelve by three.

$12 \div 3 = 4$

There are four balloons in each row.

1 Use the pictures and multiplication facts to write the division facts.

a $2 \times 4 = 8$ $\boxed{8} \div \boxed{4} = \boxed{2}$

b $7 \times 3 = 21$ $\boxed{} \div \boxed{} = \boxed{}$

c $6 \times 3 = 18$ $\boxed{} \div \boxed{} = \boxed{}$

d $7 \times 4 = 28$ $\boxed{} \div \boxed{} = \boxed{}$

2 Use the multiplication facts to write the division facts.

a $6 \times 4 = 24$ so $24 \div 4 = \boxed{6}$

b $6 \times 3 = 18$ so $18 \div 3 = \boxed{}$

c $5 \times 4 = 20$ so $20 \div \boxed{} = \boxed{}$

d $8 \times 3 = 24$ so $24 \div \boxed{} = \boxed{}$

e $9 \times 4 = 36$ so $\boxed{} \div 4 = \boxed{}$

3 Write a division fact for each picture.

a

$\boxed{16} \div \boxed{4} = \boxed{4}$

b

$\boxed{} \div \boxed{} = \boxed{}$

c

$\boxed{} \div \boxed{} = \boxed{}$

d

$\boxed{} \div \boxed{} = \boxed{}$

◆ I can use my times tables to divide numbers by three and four. $\boxed{}$

Let's try this!

Choose a division fact for dividing by three or four and draw it as a picture.

Here is a picture to show the division fact:
$18 \div 3 = 6$

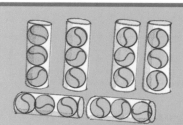

SOLVING PROBLEMS

4.1 Addition problems

● I can solve one-step problems using addition.

Key words
problem, add, total, altogether, how many?

A bag of sweets holds **twelve** chocolates and **seven** toffees.

How many sweets are there **altogether** in the bag?

The word 'altogether' tells you to **add** the numbers.

$$12 + 7 = 19$$

There are 19 sweets altogether.

Lewis swam **six** lengths on Saturday and **eight** lengths on Sunday.

Work out the **total** number of lengths he swam.

The word 'total' tells you to **add** the numbers.

$$6 + 8 = 14$$

Lewis swam a total of 14 lengths.

For each of these number problems write the addition and work out the answer.

1 Jake cycled five laps of the track on Monday and eight laps on Tuesday.

How many laps did he cycle altogether?

$$5 + 8 = 13$$

2 A farmer picked 50 red apples and 30 green apples.

What was the total number of apples he picked?

3 Nahida had 16 DVDs. She bought four more DVDs.
How many DVDs did she have altogether?

4 Kiera rolled two 10-sided dice.
She scored eight on one die and seven on
the other. What was her total score?

5 There are 20 biscuits in a packet of ginger
snaps. There are 30 biscuits in a packet of
coconut swirls.
How many biscuits are there altogether?

6 A shop sold 12 salami pizzas and
23 mushroom pizzas on Friday.
What was the total number of pizzas
sold on Friday?

7 There are 21 oranges and 27 mangoes in
these boxes of fruit.
How many are there in total?

◆ I can solve one-step problems using addition.

Let's try this!

Here is an addition.

Write three different number
problems that use this addition.

$$14 + 7 = 21$$

Subtraction problems

- I can solve one-step problems using subtraction.

There are **10** sweets in a jar. Sam eats **three** of the sweets. **How many** sweets are **left**?

The word 'left' tells you to **subtract** 3 from 10.

$$10 - 3 = 7$$

7 sweets are left.

John is **10** years old. His mother is **40** years old. What is the **difference** in their ages?

The word 'difference' tells you to **subtract** 10 from 40.

$$40 - 10 = 30$$

The difference in their ages is 30 years.

For each of these number problems write the subtraction and work out the answer.

1 Amy bought a tray of 12 eggs. She used four of them to bake a cake. How many eggs were left?

$$12 - 4 = 8$$

2 There were 18 lemon drops in a tube. Jack ate seven lemon drops. How many lemon drops were left in the tube?

3 Sam bought a note pad with 80 pages. He tore off 23 pages. How many were left?

4 A box of matches has 98 matches. Nine were used up. How many are left in the box?

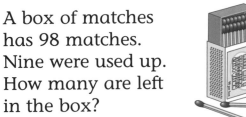

5 Liam scored 20 goals last season but Sol only scored 11 goals. What is the difference in the number of goals they scored?

6 Jamie had a box of 40 strawberries. He used 10 of them to make a strawberry smoothie. How many strawberries were left?

7 Last month it rained for 18 days and was sunny for 12 days. What is the difference between the number of rainy days and sunny days?

8 There were 35 people on a bus.
Twelve people got off the bus.
How many people were left on the bus?

◆ I can solve one-step problems using subtraction.

Let's try this!

Here is a subtraction.

50 – 20 = 30

Write three different number problems that use this subtraction.

4.3 Multiplication problems

I can solve one-step problems using multiplication.

Key words
problem, multiply, lots, how many?

A packet holds **five** pencils. **How many** pencils are there in **four** packets?

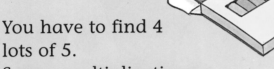

You have to find 4 lots of 5.
So use multiplication:

$$5 \times 4 = 20$$

There are 20 pencils.

Charlie buys **six** bunches of bananas. There are **three** bananas in a bunch. **How many** bananas does Charlie buy?

You have to find 6 lots of 3.
So use multiplication:

$$6 \times 3 = 18$$

There are 18 bananas.

---

1 Kyle had four pairs of shoes in his wardrobe. How many shoes were in the wardrobe?

$$4 \times 2 = 8$$

2 A bag holds five carrots. How many carrots are there in 6 bags?

3 A pepperoni pizza has eight slices of pepperoni. How many slices of pepperoni are there in five pizzas?

4 One plate holds four chocolate swirls. How many chocolate swirls can four plates hold?

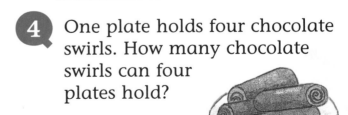

5 There were three peppers in a pack.
Bethany bought 3 packs of peppers.
How many peppers did she buy?

6 A baker made seven trays of doughnuts.
There were 10 doughnuts on each tray.
How many doughnuts did the baker make?

7 Niall bought seven bags of onions.
Each bag held four onions.
How many onions did Niall buy?

8 There are three bananas in a bunch.
How many bananas are there in nine
bunches?

9 Rachael bought eight packs of tennis balls.
Each pack holds three balls.
How many balls did Rachael buy?

◆ I can solve one-step problems using multiplication.

Let's try this!

Think of some foods that are bought in packs.
Perhaps a pack of four yoghurts or a box of 10 fish fingers.
Write some multiplication problems about them.

4.4 Division problems

● I can solve one-step problems using division.

Key words
problem, divide,
share, how many?

There are **20 biscuits** on a plate. **Four** friends **share** them equally. **How many** biscuits does each friend get?

You have to find 20 shared by 4. So divide 20 by 4:

$$20 \div 4 = 5$$

Each friend gets 5 biscuits.

There are **six** eggs in a box. A chef uses **two** eggs to make an omelette. **How many** omelettes can he make?

This problem is also about sharing. So divide 6 by 2:

$$6 \div 2 = 3$$

The chef can make 3 omelettes.

1 There are 10 pencils in a packet. The teacher shares the pencils equally between two children. How many pencils does each child get?

$$10 \div 2 = 5$$

2 Three friends share a bunch of grapes. There are 30 grapes in the bunch. How many grapes does each friend get?

3 A group of 20 players bought one box of hockey sticks. Each box contains 100 hockey sticks. The players shared the sticks equally between them. How many did each get?

4 There were eight chocolate eggs in a jar. The chocolate eggs were shared equally amongst four children. How many chocolate eggs did each child get?

5 Olivia makes bracelets. She uses five beads on each bracelet. She has 40 beads. How many bracelets can she make?

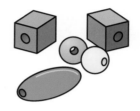

6 A library bought 80 new books. The librarian put 10 books on each shelf. How many shelves were needed for the books?

7 A baker made 28 hot cross buns. He put four buns into each box. How many boxes of buns did he fill?

◆ I can solve one-step problems using division.

Let's try this!

There are 20 biscuits on the plate.
How many people can share the biscuits equally?
Find as many answers as you can.

Money problems

I can solve one-step problems about money.

Key words
problem, cost,
change, value, total

Here are three coins.
Their total value is 65p.

50p + 10p + 5p = 65p

Yasmin buys an apple for 15p
and pays for it with a 20p coin.
How much change does she get?

20p – 15p = 5p

Yasmin gets 5p change.

1 Write the total value of the coins in each purse.

a

b

c

d

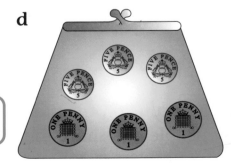

2 Find the total cost of the pieces of fruit.

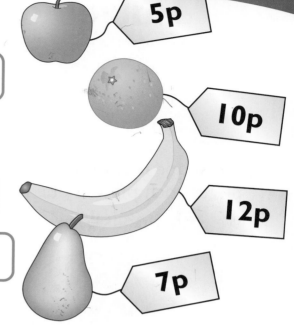

a One apple and one orange   5p + 10p = 15p

b Two oranges

c One banana and one pear

d One banana and one orange

3 How much change do you get?

a Rubber   5p – 4p = 1p

b Ruler

c Sharpener

d Pencil

◆ I can solve one-step problems about money.

FRACTIONS

5.1 Halves and quarters

● I know about halves and quarters of shapes.

Key words
fraction, half, quarter

If a shape is cut into two equal pieces each piece is one half.

We write this as $\frac{1}{2}$.

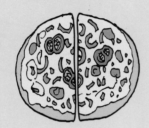

If a shape is cut into four equal pieces each piece is one quarter.

We write this as $\frac{1}{4}$.

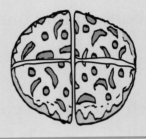

1 One half or quarter of these shapes is coloured. Write $\frac{1}{2}$ or $\frac{1}{4}$ under each shape.

a
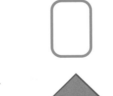

$\frac{1}{4}$

b
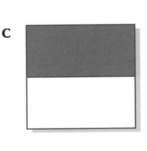

c

d

e
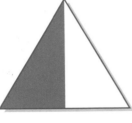

f
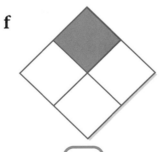

g
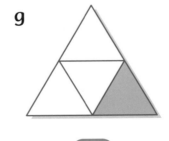

h
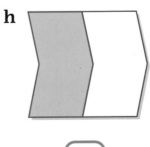

2 Draw a line to divide each shape into two halves. Colour one half.

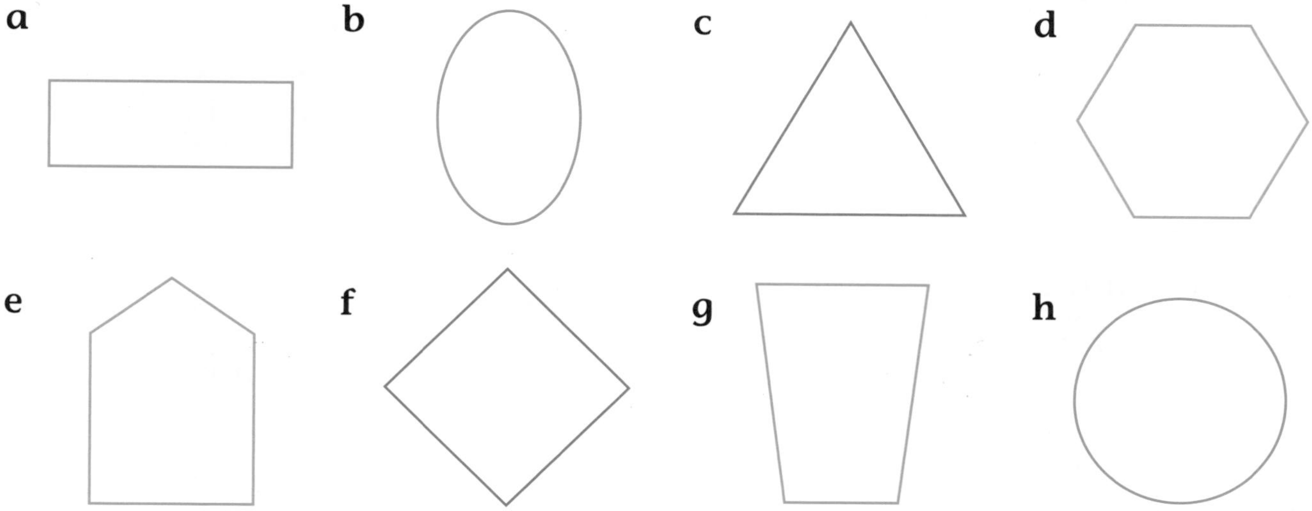

a   b   c   d

e   f   g   h

3 Draw lines to divide each shape into four quarters. Colour one quarter.

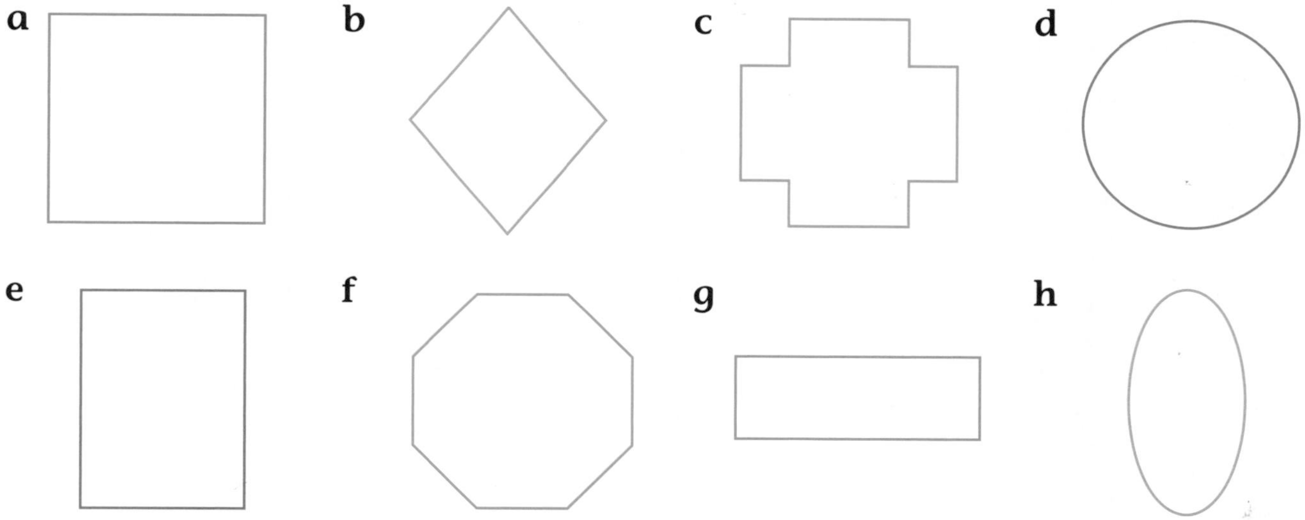

a   b   c   d

e   f   g   h

◆ I know about halves and quarters of shapes.

Let's try this!

Cut out shapes like these.
Find different ways to fold them in half.
Draw dotted lines along your folds.
Find different ways to fold them in quarters.

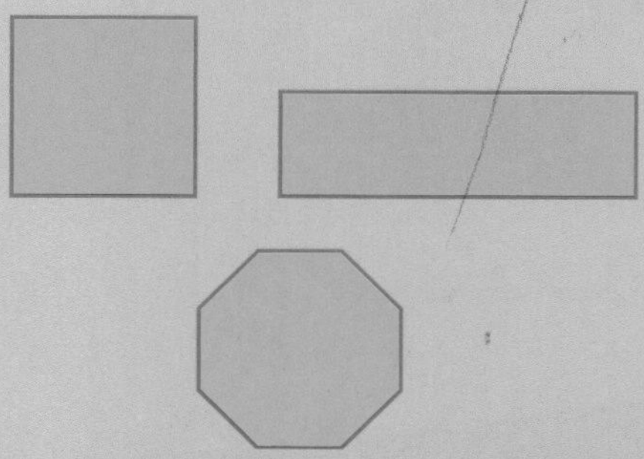

Fraction of a shape

● I know about some fractions of shapes.

Key words
fraction, numerator, denominator, third, fifth

Fractions tell you about part of a shape.

The fraction one third is written as:

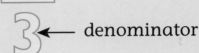

numerator → denominator

The number at the bottom is called the **denominator**. It tells you how many equal parts a thing is divided into.

The number at the top is called the **numerator**. It tells you the number of parts you have.

This circle is divided into three equal parts and one is coloured.

One third, $\frac{1}{3}$, is coloured.

This circle is divided into five equal parts and one is coloured.

One fifth, $\frac{1}{5}$, is coloured.

1 One third or one fifth of these shapes is coloured.
Write $\frac{1}{3}$ or $\frac{1}{5}$ in the boxes.

a

b

c

d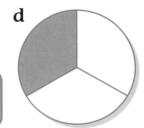

2 Colour the fraction of each shape.

a $\frac{1}{3}$ b $\frac{1}{4}$ c $\frac{1}{5}$ d $\frac{1}{2}$

      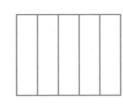   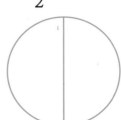

3 Write the fraction of each shape that is coloured red.

a   b   c   d

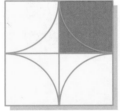         

4 Write the fraction of the shape that is coloured.

a   b   c

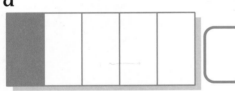      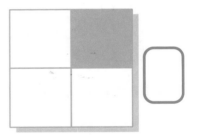

◆ I know about some fractions of shapes.

Let's try this!

This strip is divided into fifths. One fifth is coloured green.

Copy this strip on to squared paper. Cut it out and cut into five squares.

Make different shapes with your squares.
Write the fraction of your shape that is green.
Draw your shapes on squared paper.

5.3 Fraction of a number

● I can find a fraction of sets of objects.

Key words
fraction, half, quarter,
third, fifth

Here are 12 strawberries.

To find one third of
the strawberries you need
to share them into three
equal groups.

Each group has 4 strawberries so $\frac{1}{3}$ of 12 is 4.

Here are 15 pears.

To find one fifth of
the pears you need to
share them into five
equal groups.

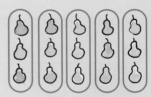

Each group has 3 pears so $\frac{1}{5}$ of 15 is 3.

1 Get some paper clips and three pots.
Share the paper clips between the three pots to find $\frac{1}{3}$ of the paper clips.

a  $\frac{1}{3}$ of 6 is $\boxed{2}$

b  $\frac{1}{3}$ of 12 is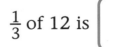

c  $\frac{1}{3}$ of 18 is ☐

d  $\frac{1}{3}$ of 9 is ☐

2 Get some paper clips and five pots.
Share the paper clips between the five pots to find $\frac{1}{5}$ of the paper clips.

a $\frac{1}{5}$ of 10 is ☐

b $\frac{1}{5}$ of 20 is ☐

c $\frac{1}{5}$ of 25 is ☐

3 Here are some sets of things. Work out the fraction of each set of things.

a $\frac{1}{3}$ of 9 is **3**

b $\frac{1}{5}$ of 10 is ☐

c $\frac{1}{3}$ of 12 is ☐

d $\frac{1}{5}$ of 15 is ☐

 I can find a fraction of sets of objects. ☐

Let's try this!

Get 10 paper clips and share them equally into three pots. Can you put an equal number of paper clips into each pot or are there any left over?
Try this again for different numbers of paper clips. Which numbers can be shared equally into the three pots? Make a list of these numbers.

5.4 More fractions

- I know about fractions of shapes where more than one part is coloured.

Key words

fraction, numerator, denominator

Here is a shape divided into four equal parts.
Two parts are coloured.

The fraction that is coloured is
two quarters.
We write this as $\frac{2}{4}$.

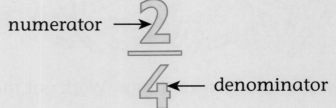

numerator

denominator

The number at the bottom is called the denominator.
It shows that the shape is divided into four equal parts.

The number at the top is called the numerator.
It shows you that you have two parts.

This shape is divided into five equal parts.
Three parts are coloured. So $\frac{3}{5}$ of the shape is coloured.

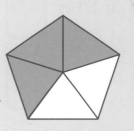

1 Each shape is divided into five equal parts, or fifths.
Colour each shape to show the fraction.

a $\frac{2}{5}$

b $\frac{4}{5}$

c $\frac{1}{5}$

d $\frac{3}{5}$

2 Each shape is divided into equal parts. Colour each shape to show the fraction.

a $\frac{2}{3}$

b $\frac{3}{4}$

c $\frac{3}{5}$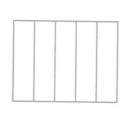

d $\frac{2}{4}$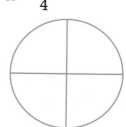

3 For each cake write the fraction that is left.

a 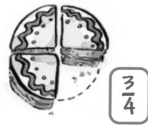 $\frac{3}{4}$

b

c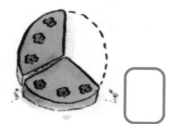

4 Each cheese is divided into fifths. Write the fraction of the cheese that is covered in brown paper.

a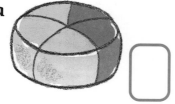

b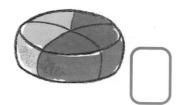

c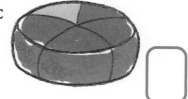

◆ I know about fractions of shapes where more than one part is coloured.

Let's try this!

Use number cards 1, 2, 3, 4, 5 to make as many different fractions as possible.
The numerator (number at the top) must be smaller than the denominator (number at the bottom).

5.5 Tenths

● I can find a tenth of a shape.

This cake is divided into ten equal pieces.

Each piece is one tenth.

We write this as $\frac{1}{10}$.

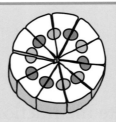

This shape is divided into tenths. Three parts are coloured.

The fraction that is shaded is three tenths. We write this as $\frac{3}{10}$.

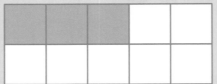

1 Each of the shapes is divided into tenths. Colour the fraction.

a $\frac{7}{10}$

b $\frac{2}{10}$

c $\frac{9}{10}$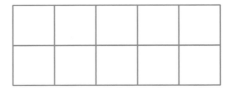

d $\frac{6}{10}$

e $\frac{1}{10}$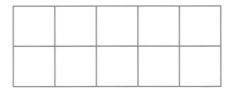

f $\frac{5}{10}$

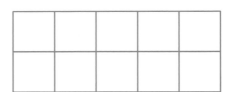

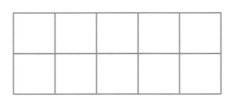

2 For each of these shapes, write the fraction that is coloured.

a

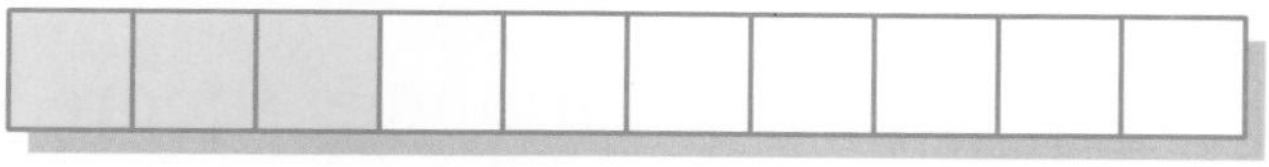

$\frac{3}{10}$

b

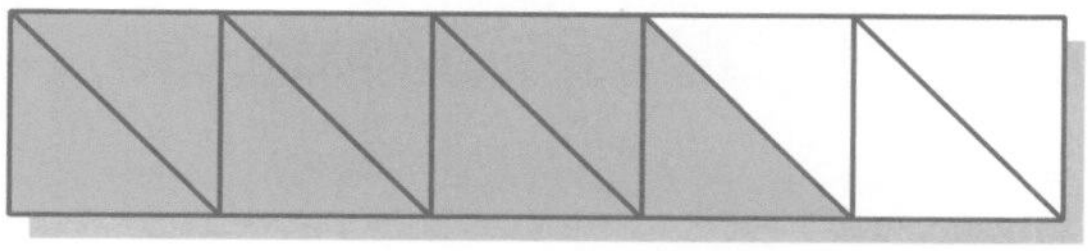

[ ]

c

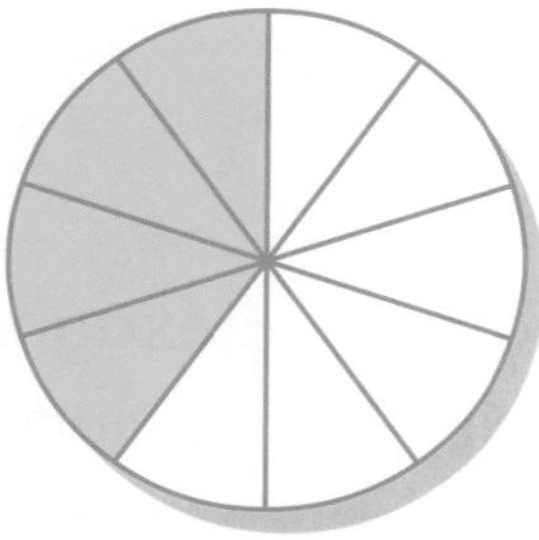

[ ]

d

[ ]

3 Each cake has been cut into tenths and some pieces have been eaten. Write the fraction of the cake that has been eaten.

a

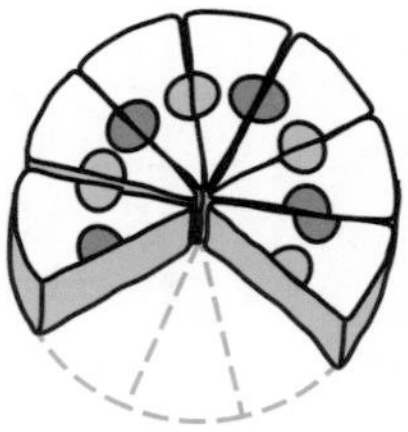

$\frac{3}{10}$

b

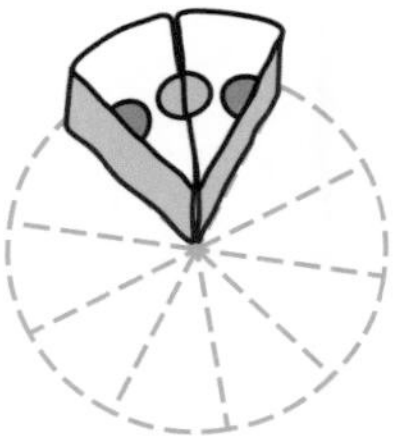

[ ]

c

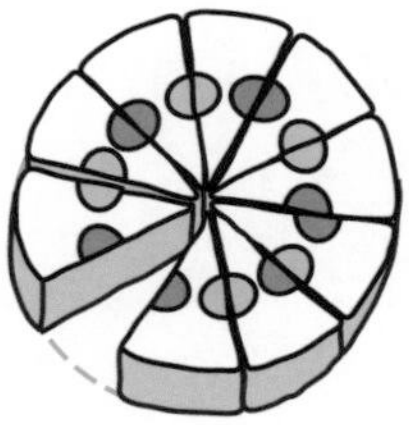

[ ]

d

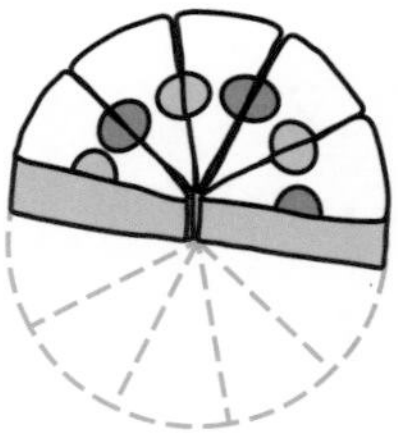

[ ]

e

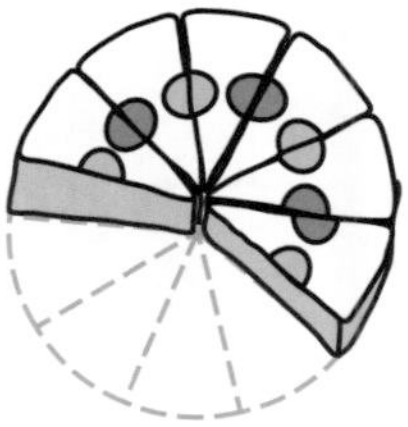

[ ]

f

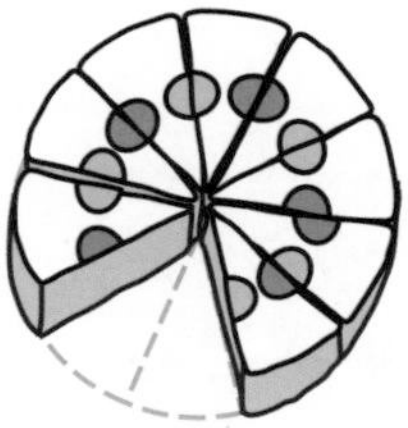

[ ]

◆ I can find a tenth of a shape. [ ]

Let's try this!

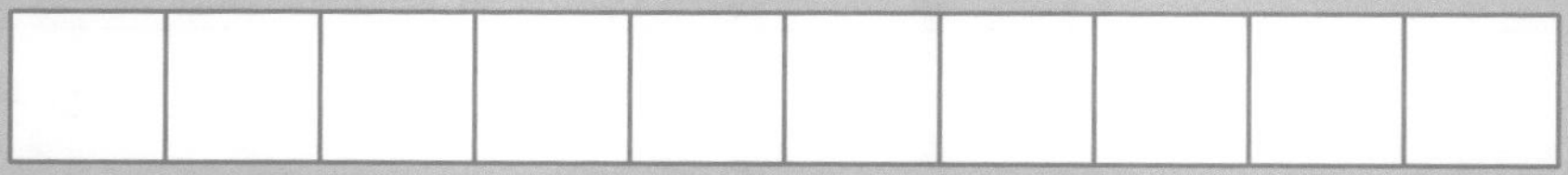

Here is a strip of 10 squares. Copy this strip onto squared paper 10 times. Find 10 different ways to colour $\frac{3}{10}$ of it.

UNDERSTANDING SHAPES

6.1 Naming 2-D shapes

● I know about 2-D shapes.

Key words
circle, triangle, square, rectangle, pentagon, hexagon, octagon, side

circle	triangle	square	rectangle	pentagon	hexagon	octagon
1 side	3 sides	4 sides	4 sides	5 sides	6 sides	8 sides

1 Get a ruler and a pencil.
Join the numbered dots.
Write the name of the shapes in the boxes.

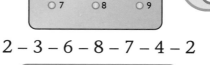

4 – 6 – 9 – 7 – 4

rectangle

a
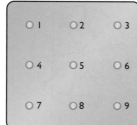

4 – 2 – 6 – 8 – 4

b
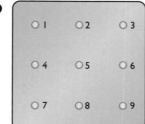

4 – 3 – 9 – 4

c
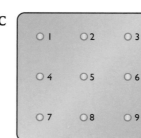

2 – 3 – 6 – 8 – 7 – 4 – 2

d

4 – 2 – 6 – 9 – 7 – 4

e
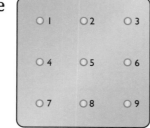

1 – 2 – 6 – 5 – 8 – 4 – 1

f
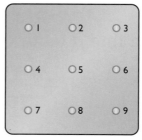

1 – 9 – 7 – 1

2 Get a ruler and a pencil.

a Draw two more different pentagons.

b Draw two more different hexagons.

c Draw two more different octagons.

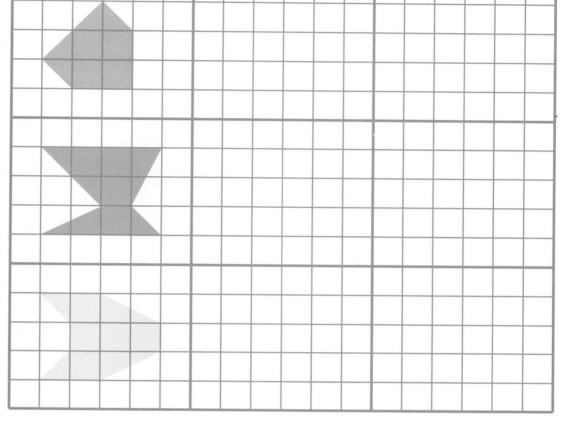

 I can name the common 2-D shapes. ☐

Let's try this!

Join the dots to make different four-sided shapes.

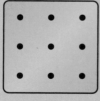 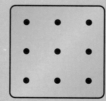  

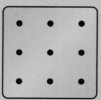 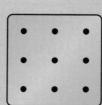 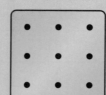 

Compass directions

- I can use the compass directions and follow instructions to make turns.

The compass points we use most are north (N), south (S), east (E) and west (W).

$\frac{1}{4}$ turn to left

$\frac{1}{4}$ turn to right

$\frac{1}{2}$ turn to right

1 Look at the picture.
Write the direction the tourist faces after these turns.

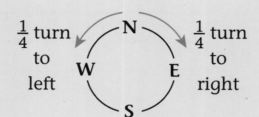
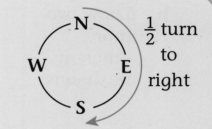

a Face north. Make a $\frac{1}{4}$ turn left.

W

b Face south. Make a $\frac{1}{2}$ turn right.

c Face east. Make a $\frac{1}{4}$ turn left.

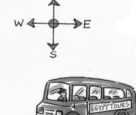

d Face west. Make a $\frac{1}{2}$ turn right.

2 Write what he will see when he makes these turns. Complete the table.

He faced the	He turned through	He now faces the
Pyramids	two $\frac{1}{4}$ turns right	
Camel	$\frac{1}{4}$ turn left	
Tour bus	$\frac{1}{4}$ turn right	
Obelisk	two $\frac{1}{4}$ turns left	

3 Write the directions for this route from A to B.

a | 2S   b |

c | d |

e | f |

g |

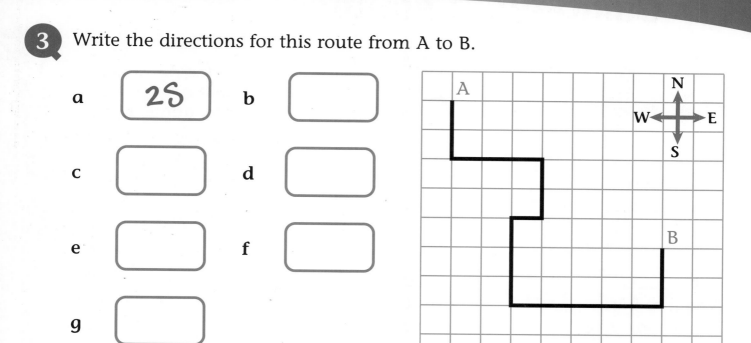

◆ I can use compass directions and follow instructions to make turns.

Let's try this!

1 Follow these directions and draw the route you take.

1	2	3	4	5	6	7	8	9
4S	2E	3N	6W	5S	8E	1N	W4	5N

2 What do you notice about your finishing point?

6.3 Using a set square

- I know about right angles in shapes and I can use a set square.

A square has:
Four equal sides and four equal corners.

Each corner is a right angle.

A right angle measures 90°.

In this square each triangle has:
a right angle (90°) and two half right angles (45°).

A set square.

1
a  b  c  d

Look at the 2-D shapes.

Write the letter of the shapes that have:

e    f

a One right angle $\boxed{b, d, j}$

g      h

b Two angles of 90°

c Four angles of 90°

i   j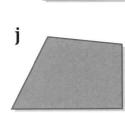

d No right angles

2 Use your set square and ruler to draw a square with 6 cm long sides.

6 cm

3 Pat takes this route from home to school. She can only walk north and east and turn through right angles.

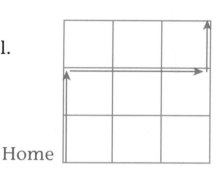

Home

School

2 north
90° turn
3 east
90° turn
1 north

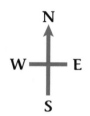

Find two more ways she can walk from home to school. Draw her routes and write the directions.

a

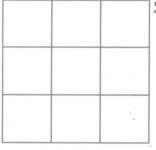

S

H

b

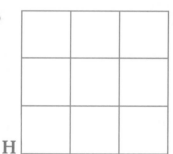

S

H

◆ I can use a set square to find right angles in shapes and make right-angled turns.

How many right angles are in these shapes?

a

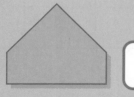

 right angles

b

right angles

Shape connections

- I can say if the sides of a shape are equal or not.

Key words
triangle, square, rectangle, pentagon, hexagon, octagon, side, right angle, vertices

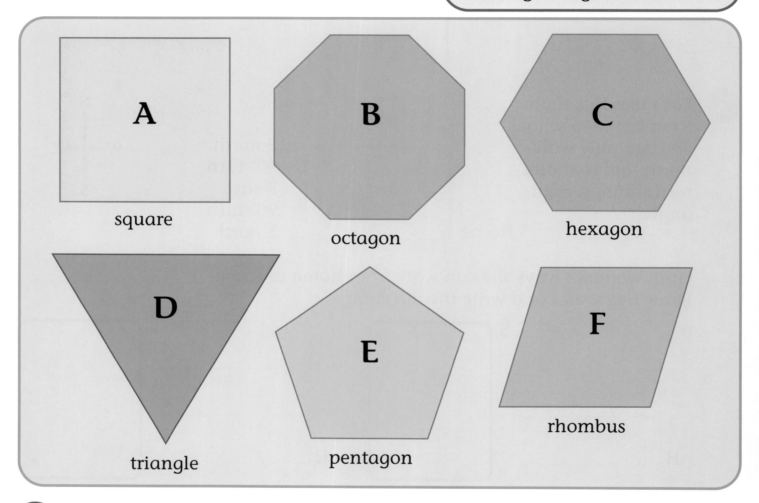

A square

B octagon

C hexagon

D triangle

E pentagon

F rhombus

1 Get a ruler.
For each shape, count the number of sides and measure the length of all the sides. Complete the table.

Shape	A	B	C	D	E	F
Number of sides	4					
Sides of the same length	4					

2 Get a blue and a red pen.
Look at these shapes.
Mark the equal sides in blue.
Circle the right angles in red.

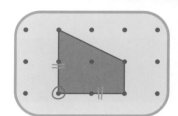

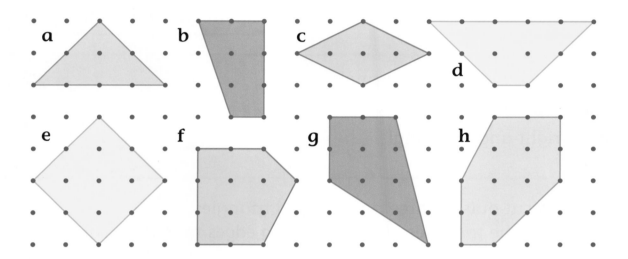

a   b   c   d

e   f   g   h

3 Look at the shapes in question 2 and complete the table.

Shape		a	b	c	d	e	f	g	h
Number of sides		3							
Number of equal sides		2							

◆ I can say whether the sides of a shape are equal or not. ☐

Let's try this!

Look at the shapes in question 2.
Read the clues and find the correct shape.

a   I have four equal sides and four right angles. ☐

b   I have one pair of equal sides and less than four corners, ☐
or vertices.

c   None of my sides is equal but I have two right angles. ☐

6.5 Creating 2-D shapes

● I can make 2-D shapes by joining identical shapes.

Key words
identical, triangle,
right-angled triangle,
square, rectangle, pentagon

When you join two identical right-angled triangles along matching edges you can make a large right-angled triangle.

1 You will need cut-outs of three right-angled triangles.
  a Join two of the triangles along matching edges to make a square.
  b Join three triangles along matching edges to make a five-sided shape.
Draw the two shapes on these dots.

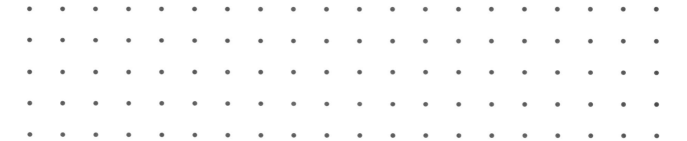

2 You will need cut-outs of four right-angled triangles.
Join your four triangles along matching edges to make:
  a a rectangle.   **b** a right-angled triangle.
  c a square.   **d** a four-sided shape with two equal sides.
Draw two of your shapes on these dots.

3 You will need cut-outs of four squares.
Join your four squares along matching edges to make:
a a rectangle.　**b** a square.　**c** a T-shape.
Draw your four shapes on these dots.

This is an L-shape

4 You can make these shapes
by joining together five squares.
Find six different shapes you can make
with five squares.
Draw them on these dots.

◆ I can make 2-D shapes when I join together two or
more identical shapes.

Let's try this!

Simon said: *"With 12 squares I can make three different rectangles."*
Is he right? Draw each different rectangle on squared paper.

MEASURE – LENGTH AND TIME

7.1 Metres and centimetres

● I know how many centimetres make 1 metre.

Key words
metre (m), half metre ($\frac{1}{2}$ m), centimetre (cm), length, distance, about

The distance between the tip of your nose and the fingertips of your outstretched hand is about 1 metre.

1 metre is equal to 100 centimetres.

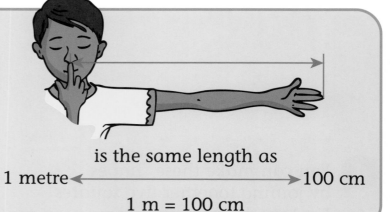

is the same length as

1 metre ⟷ 100 cm

1 m = 100 cm

1 Look at how far the golf ball is from the flag.
Write the length in centimetres.

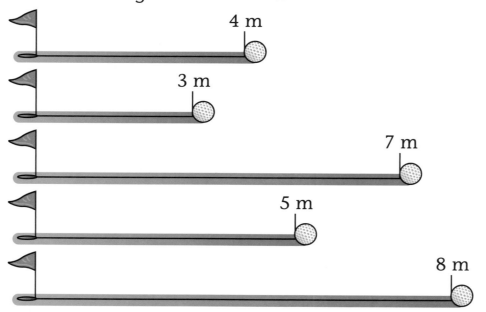

4 m

3 m

7 m

5 m

8 m

a 400 cm

b ☐ cm

c ☐ cm

d ☐ cm

e ☐ cm

2 Tiger Woods's golf ball lands on the green 11 m from the flag.

Write this distance in centimetres.

☐ cm

3 Write the missing lengths.

1 m = 100 cm $\frac{1}{2}$ m = 50 cm

1 $\frac{1}{2}$ m = 1 m 50 cm

a

3$\frac{1}{2}$ m = [3] m [50] cm	
5$\frac{1}{2}$ m = [ ] m [ ] cm	
[ ] m = 2 m 50 cm	
[ ] m = 8 m 50 cm	
15$\frac{1}{2}$ m = [ ] m [ ] cm	

b

4 m 50 cm = [ ] m
6 m 50 cm = [ ] m
[ ] m [ ] cm = 9$\frac{1}{2}$ m
[ ] m [ ] cm = 7$\frac{1}{2}$ m
12 m 50 cm = [ ] m

4 You can write a length in three ways.
Write these lengths in different ways.

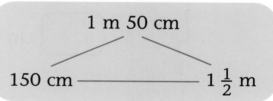

a   2 m 50 cm = [ ] m = [ ] cm

b   5$\frac{1}{2}$ m = [ ] m [ ] cm = [ ] cm

c   850 cm = [ ] m [ ] cm = [ ] m

d   10 m 50 cm = [ ] cm = [ ] m

♦ I know that 1 metre equals 100 centimetres.   [ ]

Arm span is the distance from fingertip to fingertip of outstretched arms.

Your arm span is about the same as your height.

Work as a group to test this.

7.2 Measuring to the nearest $\frac{1}{2}$ cm

I can measure lengths to the nearest $\frac{1}{2}$ cm or $\frac{1}{2}$ m.

Key words
metre (m), half metre ($\frac{1}{2}$ m), centimetre (cm), length, distance, about, nearest

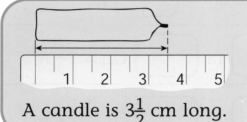

A candle is $3\frac{1}{2}$ cm long.

This candle is nearly 3 cm long. It measures $2\frac{1}{2}$ cm to the nearest $\frac{1}{2}$ cm.

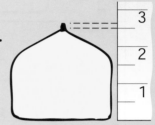

1 a Get a ruler.
Write the length of each candle to the nearest centimetre. Include the wick.

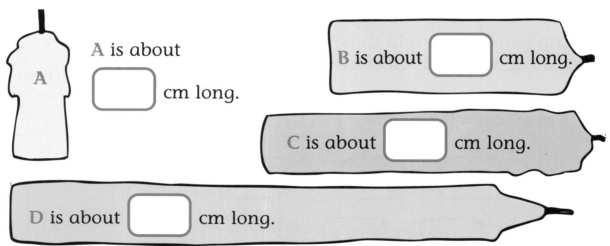

A is about ☐ cm long.

B is about ☐ cm long.

C is about ☐ cm long.

D is about ☐ cm long.

b Write the length shown by the arrow to the nearest $\frac{1}{2}$ cm.

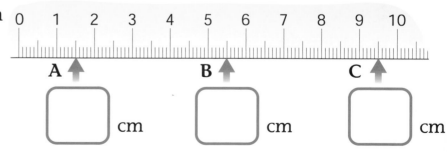

☐ cm   ☐ cm   ☐ cm

c Look at the ruler in question **1b**.
Write the ditance from: **A to B** = ☐ cm   **B to C** = ☐ cm

A to C = ☐ cm

2 Look at the scale then measure the height or length to the nearest centimetre.

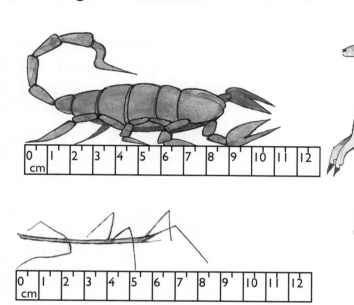

Scorpion [ ] cm

Stick insect [ ] cm

Kangaroo [ ] cm

Flamingo [ ] cm

3 **a** Measure how high each flea can jump to the nearest $\frac{1}{2}$ cm.

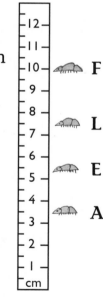

F = [10] cm L = [ ] cm E = [ ] cm A = [ ] cm

b Flea F jumped [ ] cm higher than flea L.

c Flea E jumped 2 cm higher than flea [ ].

d Flea A jumped 4 cm lower than flea [ ].

◆ I can measure lengths to the nearest $\frac{1}{2}$ cm. [ ]

Let's try this!

A carpenter has three lengths of wood measuring 3 metres, $4\frac{1}{2}$ metres and $6\frac{1}{2}$ metres.

If he joins any two lengths of wood, what different lengths can he make?

Which standard unit?

- I can choose different units to measure length.
- I can solve problems about length.

Key words

metre (m), half metre ($\frac{1}{2}$ m), centimetre (cm), length, height, width, thickness, depth, distance, estimate

Small things are measured in centimetres.

Larger items are measured in metres.

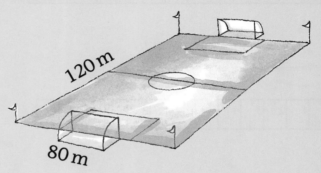

1 Circle what you would use to measure:

a the length of a bus.   cm   m

b the height of a goal mouth.   cm   m

c the width of a bus ticket.   cm   m

d the thickness of a sandwich.   cm   m

e the length of a football scarf.   cm   m

f the height of a window.   cm   m

g the top of a dice.   cm   m

2 Circle the best estimate.

a Height of door

$\frac{1}{2}$ m   2 $\frac{1}{2}$ m   4 m

b Distance between taps

5 cm   10 cm   20 cm

c Width of paper towel

5 cm   10 cm   20 cm

d height of waste bin

$\frac{1}{2}$ m   2 m   5 m

3

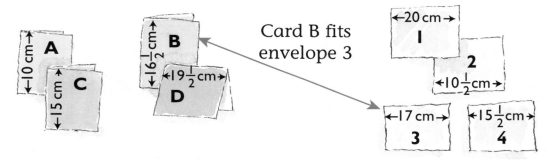

Card B fits envelope 3

a Card A fits envelope ☐

b Card B fits envelope ☐ 3

c Card C fits envelope ☐

d Card D fits envelope ☐

◆ I can choose suitable units to measure length and solve problems about length. ☐

Let's try this!

Helen's lunch box is 25 cm long.

She said, *"If I have another seven identical lunch boxes and place them end to end, the total length will be 2 metres."*

Is she right? Show how you worked out your answer.

Time to the quarter hour

I can tell the time to the $\frac{1}{4}$ hour on an analogue clock and a 12-hour digital clock.

Key words
time, clock, hours (h), minutes (min), half past, quarter past, quarter to, analogue, digital

1:00
1 o'clock

1:30
$\frac{1}{2}$ past 1
half past 1

1:15
$\frac{1}{4}$ past 1
quarter past 1

1:45
$\frac{1}{4}$ to 2
quarter to 2

1 Write the time each clock shows.

a

$\frac{1}{2}$ past 10

b

c

d

e

f

g

7:15

h

8:45

i

12:15

2 Look at the clues for each clock to help you tell the time.
Draw the time each clock face shows.
Circle the digital clock which shows the matching time.

a The time I show is
• 15 minutes past seven.

3:15   6:15
7:15   7:45

b The time I show is
• $\frac{1}{4}$ past the hour.

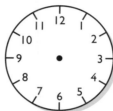

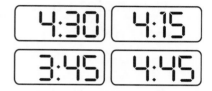

4:30   4:15
3:45   4:45

c The time I show is
• quarter to one.

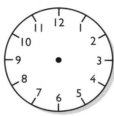

1:45   1:15
1:00   12:45

d The time I show is
• earlier than 8 o'clock and
• later than 7 o'clock.

8:15   7:00
7:45   6:45

3 Continue these 15 minute patterns.

a 3:00, 3:15, 3:30,  , 4:30.

b 8:30, 8:45; 9:00,  .

 I can tell the time to the quarter hour. ☐

Let's try this!

Write these times starting with the earliest time.

1:15   12:30   1:00   12:45   12:15   1:30

7.5 Time to the nearest 5 minutes

● I can tell the time to the $\frac{1}{4}$ hour on an analogue clock and a 12-hour digital clock to the nearest 5 minutes.

This clock shows 10 minutes past 5 or 10 past 5.

This clock shows 20 minutes to 3 or 20 to 3.

1 Write the missing 5 minute intervals in the circles.

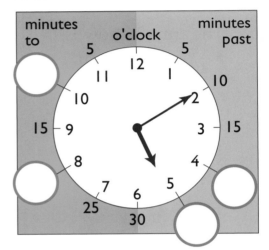

2 Write these times.

a

b

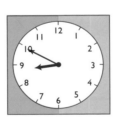

c

d

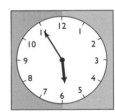

5 past 11

Now write what time each clock will show in one hour's time.

clock **a**   5 past ◯   clock **b**

clock **c**    clock **d**

3 Show the time on these digital clocks.

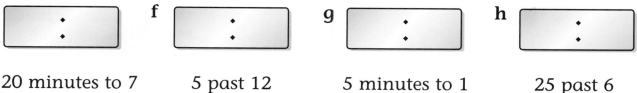

a **4 : 10**

10 minutes past 4   b 25 to 9   c 20 past 8   d 10 minutes to 2

e 20 minutes to 7   f 5 past 12   g 5 minutes to 1   h 25 past 6

4 Draw and write the times on both clocks.

a 10 past 4   b 25 to 9   c 20 past 3   d 10 to 11

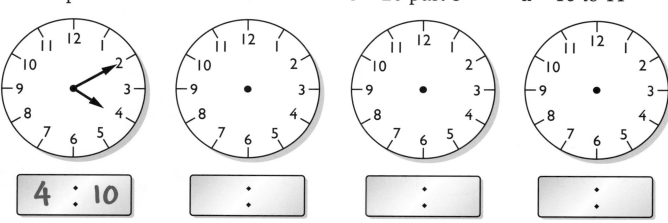

4 : 10

◆ I can read the time to the nearest 5 minutes. ☐

Let's try this!

This is the school clock.

a Write the digital time it showed:

   10 minutes ago. [:]

   20 minutes ago. [:]

b In a quarter of an hour's
   time when the school bell rings it will be [:]

Measure – Weight, Capacity and Time

8.1 Grams and kilograms

I know how many grams make one kilogram and can solve problems about weight.

Key words
gram (g), kilogram (kg), weigh

A 1 kg bag of flour weighs the same as two 500 g packs of pasta.

$$1 \text{ kg} = 500 \text{ g} + 500 \text{ g}$$
$$= 1000 \text{ g}$$
$$\text{or } 1 \text{ kg} = \tfrac{1}{2} \text{ kg} + \tfrac{1}{2} \text{ kg}$$

1 You can write a weight in three ways.
Write these weights in different ways.

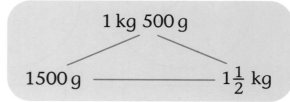

1 kg 500 g

1500 g ——— $1\tfrac{1}{2}$ kg

a 5 kg 500 g = $\boxed{5\tfrac{1}{2}}$ kg = $\boxed{5500}$ g

b $4\tfrac{1}{2}$ kg = ☐ kg ☐ g = ☐ g

c 3500 g = ☐ kg ☐ g = ☐ kg

d 7 kg 500 g = ☐ kg = ☐ g

e $9\tfrac{1}{2}$ kg = ☐ kg ☐ g = ☐ g

f 8500 g = ☐ kg ☐ g = ☐ kg

2 Ron's vegetable bag has 1 bag of carrots, 2 bags of onions and 1 pepper.

carrots	500 g
onions	200 g
onions	200 g
pepper	100 g
Total	1000 g or 1 kg

100 g

200 g

200 g

500 g

Fill in the table so that each vegetable bag weighs 1 kg.

Vegetable bag	Carrots 500 g	Onions 200 g	Pepper 100 g	Working out
a	1	2	1	500 g + 200 g + 200 g + 100 g = 1000 g
b	1	1		500 g +
c	1	0		
d	0	4		
e	0	3		
f	0		6	
g	0		8	

3 Look at the pictures and weights of potatoes, carrots, onions and pepper. Find the total weight in grams of:

a 1 bag potatoes + 1 bag of onions + 1 pepper = ☐ g

b 1 bag of carrots + 2 bags of onions = ☐ g

2500 g

◆ I can convert grams to kilograms and solve problems. ☐

Let's try this!

5 oranges weigh $1\frac{1}{2}$ kg.

How many grams does one orange weigh? ☐

Using scales

● I can read numbers on a scale to the nearest 100 g.

Key words
gram (g), kilogram (kg), weigh, scale, nearest, about

The arrow shows the weight of the book to the nearest 100 g.

The arrow is pointing half way between 200 g and 400 g.

So the book weighs 300 g.

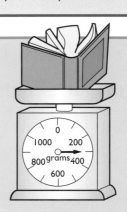

1 Write the weight shown on the scales to the nearest 100 grams.

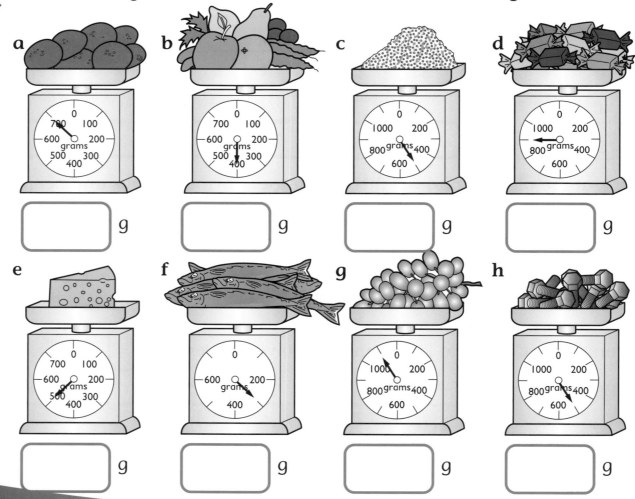

a ____ g

b ____ g

c ____ g

d ____ g

e ____ g

f ____ g

g ____ g

h ____ g

2 These foods weigh just over or just under a multiple of 100 g.
Find each weight to the nearest 100 g.

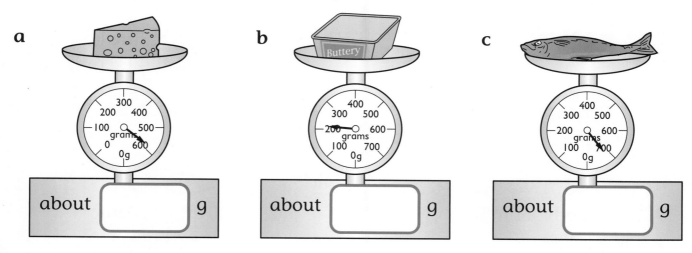

a about ☐ g

b about ☐ g

c about ☐ g

3 Write the weight shown on these scales.

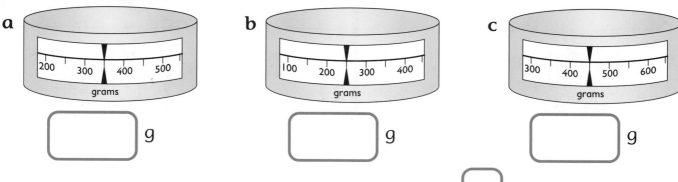

a ☐ g

b ☐ g

c ☐ g

◆ I can read numbers on a scale to the nearest 100 g. ☐

Let's try this!

In the middle box write the weight shown on the scales.

Half and double each weight and write your answers in the correct boxes.

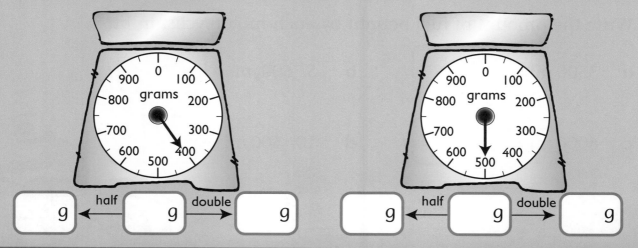

☐ g ← half ☐ g double → ☐ g

☐ g ← half ☐ g double → ☐ g

8.3 Litres and millilitres

- I know how many millilitres make one litre.
- I can solve problems about capacity.

 = +

A 1 litre bottle of milk holds the same amount as two 500 ml bottles of cola.

$1l = 500\,\text{ml} + 500\,\text{ml}$
$= 1000\,\text{ml}$
or $1l = \frac{1}{2}\,l + \frac{1}{2}\,l$

1

a $1\frac{1}{2}\,l$ b $2\frac{1}{2}\,l$ c $4\frac{1}{2}\,l$ d $8\frac{1}{2}\,l$

These labels show the amount of fuel in each fuel tank.
Write the amount in millilitres.

a $1\frac{1}{2}\,l = \boxed{1500}$ ml

b $2\frac{1}{2}\,l = \boxed{}$ ml

c $4\frac{1}{2}\,l = \boxed{}$ ml

d $8\frac{1}{2}\,l = \boxed{}$ ml

2 Write the amount of fuel bought by each motorcyclist in litres.

a $3500\,\text{ml} = \boxed{}$ l

b $5l\ 500\,\text{ml} = \boxed{}$ l

c $6000\,\text{ml} = \boxed{}$ l

d $10l\ 500\,\text{ml} = \boxed{}$ l

3 Look at the capacity marked on each container. Complete the following statements.

A 100 ml

B $\frac{1}{2}$ l

C 250 ml

D 1000 ml

E $\frac{1}{10}$ l

F $1\frac{1}{2}$ l

G 1 l

H 500 ml

I $\frac{1}{4}$ l

a A has the same capacity as ☐ .

b B has the same capacity as ☐ .

c C has the same capacity as ☐ .

d D has the same capacity as ☐ .

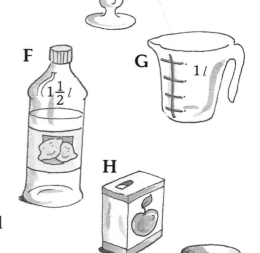

4 Fill in the missing capacities.

a 1 l = 1000 ml

b $\frac{1}{2}$ l = ☐ ml

c $\frac{1}{4}$ l = ☐ ml

d $\frac{1}{10}$ l = ☐ ml

 I can say how many millilitres make one litre. ☐

Let's try this!

How many times can you:

a fill the mug from the teapot?

b fill the clear glass from the carton of milk?

c fill the mug from the carton of apple juice.

d fill the pink glass from the bottle of lemonade.

Measuring in millilitres

● I can read numbers on a scale to the nearest 100 ml.

Key words

litre (l), $\frac{1}{2}$ litre ($\frac{1}{2}l$), $\frac{1}{4}$ litre ($\frac{1}{4}l$), millilitre (ml), capacity, scale

Look at the markings on these measuring jugs.

Both 1 litre jugs show intervals of 100 ml.

Both jugs hold 200 ml of water.

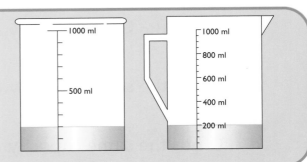

1 **a** How much water is in each measuring jug?

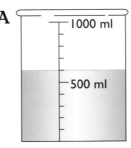 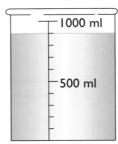 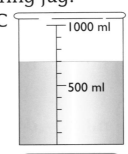 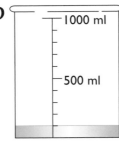

600 ml  ml  ml  ml

b Draw a line to show how much water is in each jug.

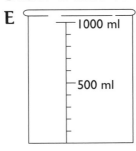 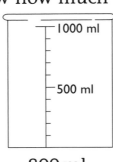 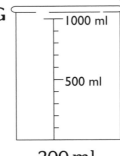 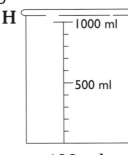

300 ml   800 ml   200 ml   400 ml

c I need to add  ml of water to jug **E** to make 1l.

d I need to add [ ] ml of water to jug **F** to make 1l.

2 Write the amount of lemonade in each bottle to the nearest 100 ml.

a 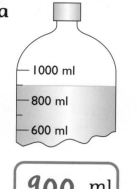   **b** 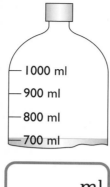   **c** 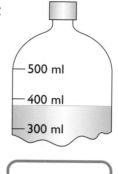   **d**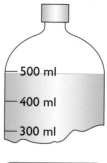

 **900** ml   _____ ml   _____ ml   _____ ml

3 Read each clue then mark the correct level on each measuring jar.

B holds $\frac{1}{2}l$ more than jar **A**.

C holds $\frac{1}{10}l$ more than jar **B**.

D holds half as much as jar **A**.

A 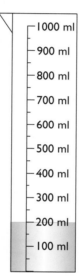   **B** 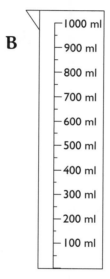   **C** 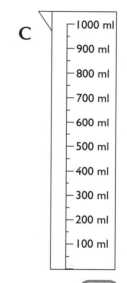   **D**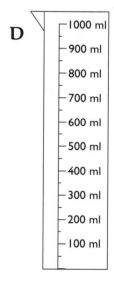

 I can read numbers on a scale to the nearest 100 ml. ☐

Let's try this!

How much paint is in the tin?

Tin	Amount of paint in ml	Amount of paint in l
A		
B		
C		
D		

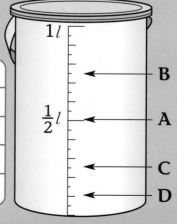

● I know about time. I can estimate how long an activity takes.

It takes about 3 minutes to boil a kettle.

 An Olympic sprinter can run 100 m in just under 10 seconds.

The flight from London to New York takes about 9 hours.

1 These numbers are used to measure time.

7	12	24	52	60	60	356

Write the correct numbers in the boxes.

a [60] seconds → 1 minute   **b** [   ] minutes → 1 hour

c [   ] days → 1 week   **d** [   ] hours → 1 day

e [   ] months → 1 year   **f** [   ] weeks → 1 year

g [   ] days → 1 year

2 Write which unit of time you would use to measure how long it takes to do the[

a Boil an egg [   ]   **b** Blink [   ]

c Watch a football match [   ]   **d** Text a friend [   ]

3 Circle the best estimate for these times.

a Eat a hamburger	(5 minutes)	15 minutes	1 hour
b A bus journey into town	20 seconds	20 minutes	2 hours
c A flight to India	1 hour	5 hours	10 hours
d A sneeze	2 seconds	30 seconds	2 minutes
e A week's holiday	10 days	7 days	14 days

4 Alan has three sweatshirts and two pairs of jeans.

Can he wear a different outfit of a sweatshirt and jeans every day of the week?
Colour his sweatshirts red, blue or grey and his jeans blue or black to find out.

Monday	Tuesday	Wednesday	Thursday	Friday	Saturday	Sunday

 I know the units of time and I can estimate how long an activity might take. ☐

Let's try this!

a Estimate and measure how long it will take you to say the five times table.

b Work with a partner. Choose a length of time between 10 and 60 seconds.
Take it in turns to stop a stopwatch at that time without looking at the watch.

MORE ON SHAPES

9.1 Symmetry in 2-D shapes

● I can say whether a shape is symmetrical or not and can draw a symmetrical shape.

Key words
mirror line, line of symmetry, reflection, symmetrical

Here are some road signs.
1. Some road signs have **no line** of symmetry.
2. Some have **one line** of symmetry.
3. Some have **more than one line** of symmetry.

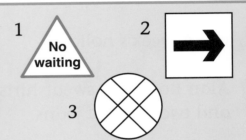

1 Get a ruler and a mirror.
For each road sign, use a ruler to draw any lines of symmetry.
Use a mirror to check. Then complete the table.

a ⬤   b ⚠️!   c **H**   d ✈️

e ◯   f ↘   g **T**   h **P**

Lines of symmetry	Road sign
None	
One	
More than one	

2 Put your mirror on the mirror line.

Write the name of the shape you make.

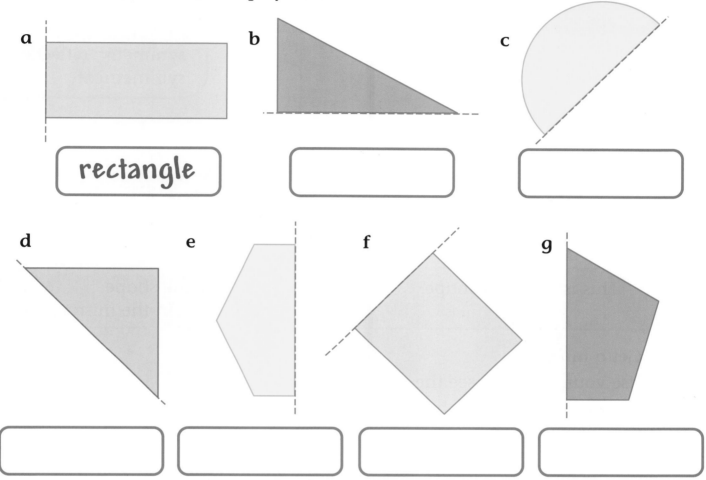

a

rectangle

b

c

d

e

f

g

◆ I can test a shape for line symmetry and draw a symmetrical shape.

Let's try this!

Get six coloured squares, 1 cm squared paper, a mirror, a ruler and a red pen.

- Find different ways to make a symmetrical pattern with your six squares.
- Draw your patterns on 1 cm squared paper.
- Mark the lines of symmetry with a dotted red line.

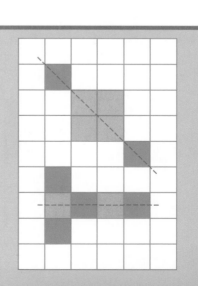

9.2 Reflecting shapes

- I can reflect a shape when the mirror line is along one edge.

Key words
mirror line, line of symmetry, reflection, symmetrical

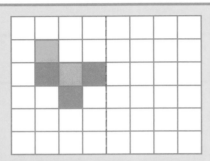

This is half of a shape.

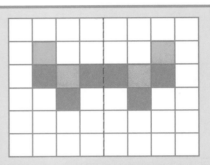

This is the shape reflected in the mirror.

1 Get a mirror.

Use your mirror to see the reflected shape.

Complete each shape by drawing the reflection.

a
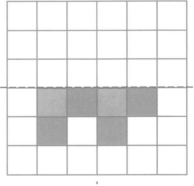

b
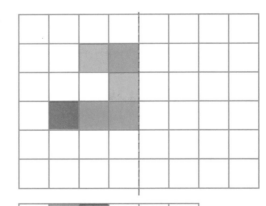

c
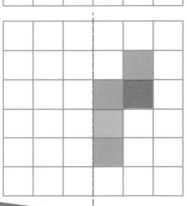

d
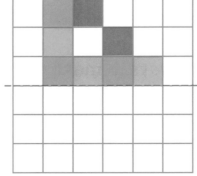

2 Draw the reflection of each half shape.

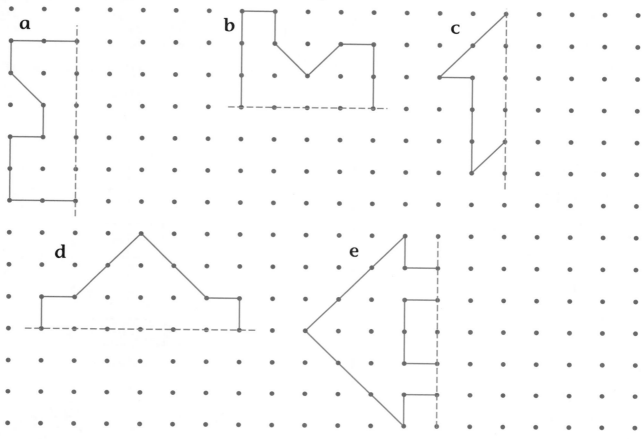

◆ I can draw the reflection of a shape when the mirror line is along one edge.

Let's try this!

Get some coloured pens, a mirror and a ruler.

Colour some of the triangles in each half shape.

Reflect the half shape in a mirror to complete each shape.

Colour the matching half shape.

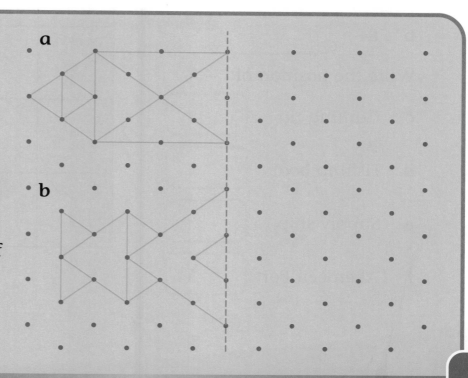

Find your position

- I can find a position on a grid.
- I can label rows and columns on a grid.

What is the position of the circle in the grid?

1 Start at the bottom left-hand corner.

2 Count along the columns, **A, B, C.**

3 Count up the rows, 1, 2, **3.**

4 The circle is in square **C3**.

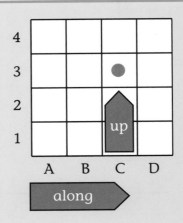

1 Look at the map of the oil rigs in the North Sea.

Write the names of the oil rigs.

a C3

b E4

Write the position of:

c Gamma rig

d Fishing boats

e Supply ship

f Aberdeen Port

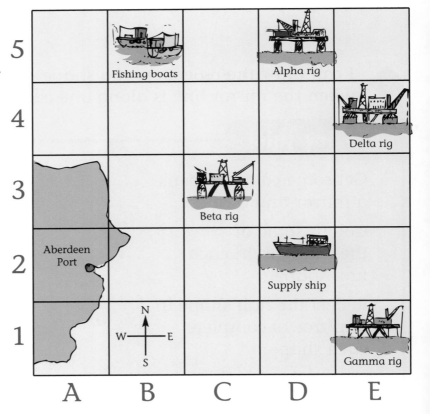

2 Write the seat number for:

a Derek [ ]   **b** Maya [ ]

c Jim [ ]   **d** Ann [ ]

e Tom [ ]   **f** Emma [ ]

g Jenny [ ]   **h** Amir [ ]

	A	B	C
4	Ann	Clare	Emma
3	Rob	Amir	Jim
2	Maya	Jenny	Sam
1	Tom	Derek	Lee

3 Write who is sitting in:

a C2 [ ]   **b** A3 [ ]

◆ I can find the position of a square on a grid of squares. [ ]

Let's try this!

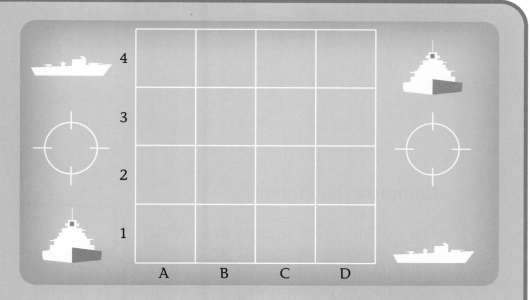

Battleships –
This is a game for two players.

You need four counters each.

- Choose four squares for your ships and put a counter in these squares.
- Don't let your partner see your grid.
- Take it in turns to call out the position of a ship, for example, C3.
- Your partner draws a circle in that square on his/her grid.
- At the end, check that the positions of the counters on your grid match the positions of the circles your partner drew on his/her grid.

9.4 Describing 3-D solids

● I can name and describe 3-D shapes.

Key words
cube, cuboid, cone, cylinder, hemisphere, triangular prism, hexagonal prism, square-based pyramid, face, edge, rectangular

A prism is the same size and shape all the way through its length.

All its faces are flat and do not get wider or narrower.

In this 3-D shape the two end faces are triangles and three faces are rectangles. It is a triangular prism.

1 Get blue, green, orange and red pencils.

a Colour the end faces of these shapes like this:

b Complete the sentences.

The rectangular prisms are coloured ☐ and ☐.

The square prisms are ☐ in colour.

The ☐ prisms are coloured blue.

The hexagonal prisms are ☐ in colour.

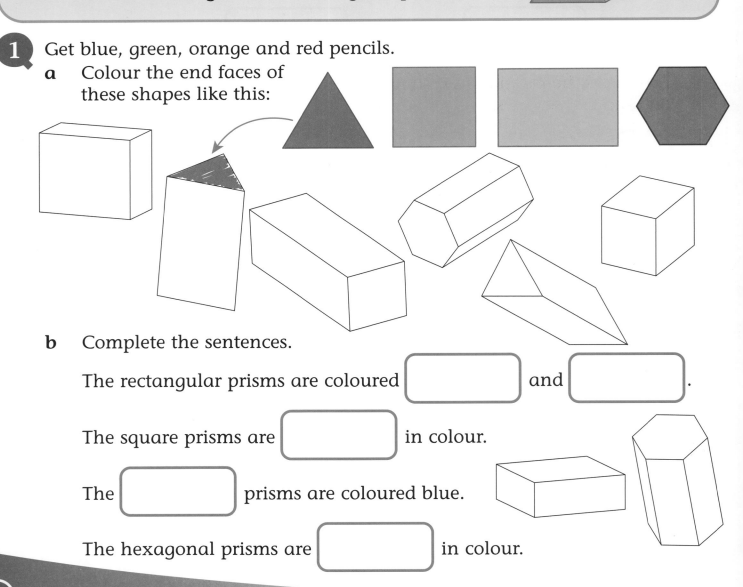

2 Put a tick [✔] in the box if the 3-D shape is a prism.

A ✔   B ☐   C ☐   D ☐

E ☐   F ☐   G ☐   H ☐

3 Write the number of faces and edges for these shapes.

a A has ☐ faces.   b B has ☐ faces.   c E has ☐ faces.

d F has ☐ edges.   e D has ☐ edges.   f H has ☐ edges.

◆ I can say whether a shape is a prism or not and count its faces and edges. ☐

Let's try this!

Complete the table.

3-D solid	Number of faces	Number of edges of an end face
Cube		
Cuboid		
Triangular prism		
Hexagonal prism		

● I know about 2-D shapes and the faces of 3-D solids.

Key words
cube, cuboid, cone, cylinder, sphere, triangular prism, hexagonal prism, square-based pyramid, face, edge, rectangular, curved, circular

1 Write in the table how many of each 2-D face you need to make each 3-D shape.

2-D faces / 3-D shape	⬤	▲	◻	▭	⬠	⬡
a				6		
b						
c						
d						
e						
f						

2

cube　　　cuboid　　　cone　　cylinder　　sphere　　triangular　　square-
　　　　　　　　　　　　　　　　　　　　　　　　　　　　　prism　　　based
　　　　　　　　　　　　　　　　　　　　　　　　　　　　　　　　　pyramid

Use the clues to write the names of the 3-D shapes.

a　1 curved face　　　　　　　　　**b**　6 faces altogether
　　2 circular faces　　　　　　　　　　　2 faces are square
　　2 curved edges　　　　　　　　　　　4 faces are rectangular

　　The shape is a ⎡ cylinder ⎤.　　　The shape is a ⎡　　　⎤.

c　2 triangular end faces　　　　　**d**　A flat base which is square
　　All other faces are rectangles　　　4 triangular faces meet at a point

　　The shape is a ⎡　　　⎤.　　　　The shape is a ⎡　　　⎤.

e　6 identical faces　　　　　　　　**f**　1 flat circular base
　　12 edges all the same length　　　　Curved sides which come to a point

　　The shape is a ⎡　　　⎤.　　　　The shape is a ⎡　　　⎤.

◆　I can match 2-D shapes to the faces of 3-D shapes. ☐

Let's try this!

Complete the table.

Prism end face	Number of sides of end face	Number of faces
Triangle	3	5
Square		
Pentagon		
Hexagon		
Octagon		

How many faces will a prism have if its
end face has seven sides? ⎡　　　⎤

HANDLING DATA

10.1 Tally charts

- I can explain what a tally chart tells us.

Keeping a tally means grouping in 5s.

This helps us to count the total or the frequency quickly and correctly.

Vehicle	Tally	Frequency
Buses	卌 卌 ||	12
Vans	卌 ||||	9

1 Harry made this table of the kinds of vehicles passing his school at lunchtime.

Transport	Number	Total
Car	||||||||||||||||||||||||||	26
Bus	|||||||||||||||||	
Motorbike	||||||||||	
Lorry / van	||||||||||||||	
Bicycle	||||||||||||	

a Complete the Total column on Harry's table.

b Use Harry's data to complete the tally and frequency column.

Transport	Tally	Frequency
Car		
Bus		
Motorbike		
Lorry / van		
Bicycle		

c How many more cars were there than buses?

d How many kinds of vehicles were two-wheeled?

2 Mary asked some people about their shopping. She then made a tally chart for her question, "Where do you go to buy your fruit and vegetables?"

Shop	Tally	Frequency
Supermarket	ΙΙΙΙ ΙΙΙΙ ΙΙΙ	
Corner shop	ΙΙΙΙ ΙΙ	
Market stall	ΙΙΙΙ ΙΙΙΙ Ι	
Greengrocer	ΙΙΙΙ	

a Complete the frequency column of Mary's table.
b Where is the most popular place to buy fruit and vegetables?

c How many more people shopped at the market stall than at the greengrocer's shop?

d How many people did Mary ask altogether?

3 Mary asked some other people, "What kind of bread do you like best?"
a Complete the tally column on Mary's chart.

b Which is the most popular kind of bread?

Bread	Tally	Frequency
White		17
Brown		20
Crusty		11
Pita		8
Naan		4

c How many people like brown bread best?

d How many more people like white bread better than crusty bread?

◆ I can show information in a tally chart.

Let's try this!

Look at the transport data on page 94.
How might Harry's chart be different if he had collected the information at 6 o'clock in the morning? Say why.

● I can show information in a pictogram.

Key words
organise, interpret,
data, table, pictogram,
most / least common

This pictogram shows how often the website holidays4u.com was visited in one week.

Number of visits	Sun	Mon	Tue	Wed	Thu	Fri	Sat
	⊢						H
	H						H
	H				H		H
	H	H			H	H	H
	H	H	H	⊢	H	H	H
	H	H	H	H	H	H	H

Key:
H = 2 visits
⊢ = 1 visit

1 a In the frequency table, write the number of times the hotels4u.com website was visited each day.

b Which day had the fewest visits?

c On which days were there more than 10 visits to the website?

Transport	Frequency
Sunday	11
Monday	
Tuesday	
Wednesday	
Thursday	
Friday	
Saturday	

d Which two days had the same number of visits?

e How many visits altogether did the website get?

2 In one day Class 9B collected these coins for the charity, 'Children in Need'.

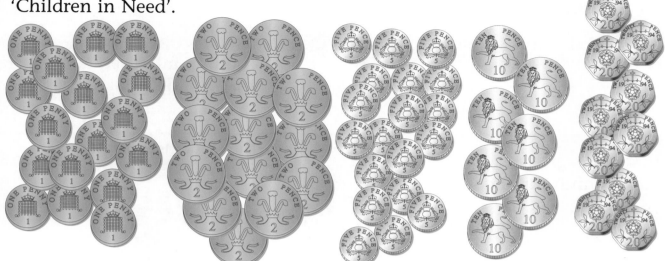

a Count how many 1p, 2p, 5p, 10p and 20p coins they collected.

b Complete the coins pictogram.

Coin	Number
1p	
2p	
5p	
10p	
20p	

Coins collected for 'Children in Need'

20p

10p

5p

2p

1p

Number of coins

Key: ◯ = 2 coins

c The most common coin is ☐ p. The least common coin is ☐ p.

◆ I can explain what a pictogram represents. ☐

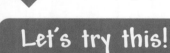

Draw a pictogram to show how much money Class 9B collected the next day.

Coin	1p	2p	5p	10p	20p	50p
Number	6	12	16	9	14	8

10.3 Block graphs

● I can show information in tables and block graphs.

Key words
organise, interpret, data, table, block graph, title, label, scale

In a block graph, each block stands for one unit.

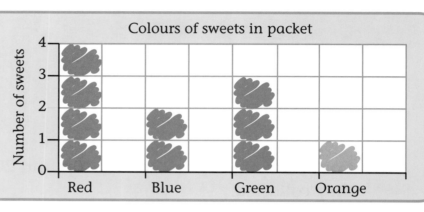

Colours of sweets in packet

1 a Count how many of each kind of can there are.

Can	Number
Cherry	5
Cola	
Lemonade	
Orange	

b Now complete the graph to show the number of cans for each drink.

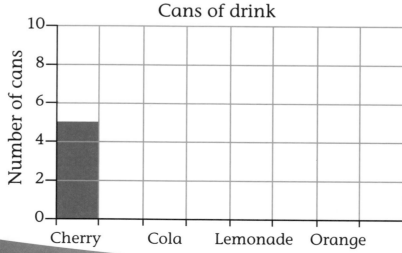

Cans of drink

2 Look at the capacities on these containers.
Complete the block graph.
The first one has been done for you.

a

APPLE JUICE 1 LITRE

b

COLA 500 ml

c

SALAD DRESSING 200ml

d

TOMATO SAUCE 100ml

e

SHAMPOO 400 ml

Container capacities

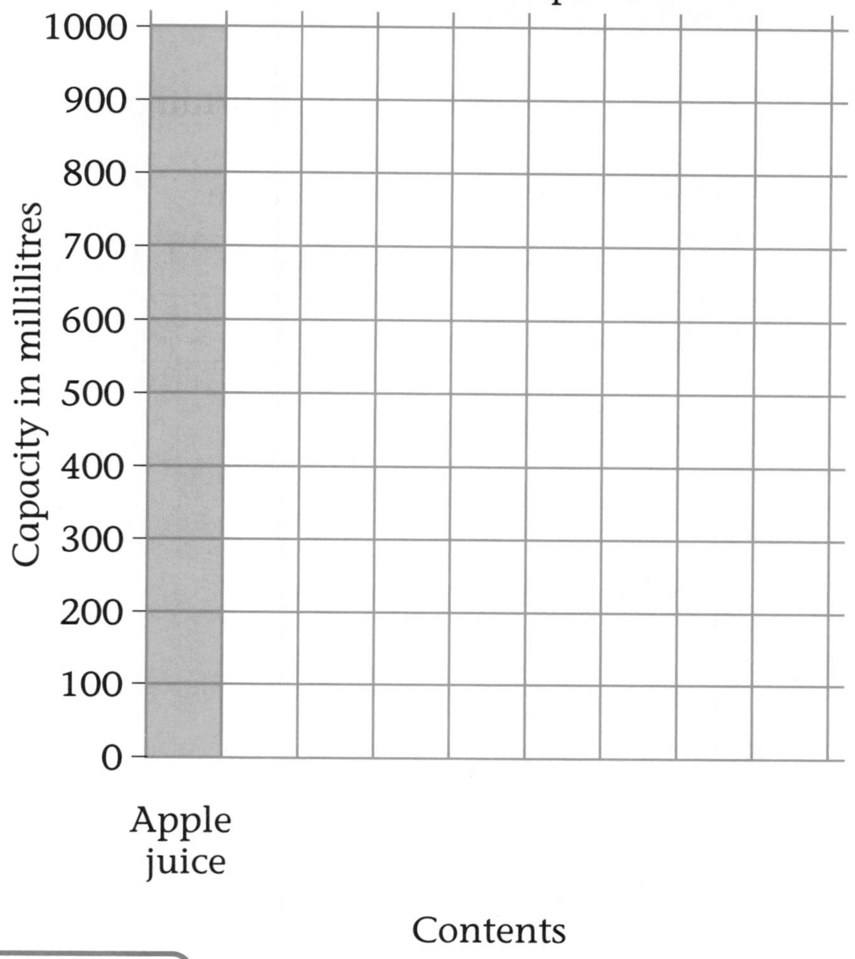

Capacity in millilitres

1000
900
800
700
600
500
400
300
200
100
0

Apple juice

Contents

3 **a** The bottle of [ ] holds the least.

b The middle-sized container is filled with [ ].

c The bottle of shampoo holds twice as much as the bottle of [ ].

◆ I can show information in tables and block graphs. [ ]

Let's try this!

Draw a pictogram for the data about the cans on page 98.
Draw one can for every two blocks in the graph.

- I can show information using tables and bar charts.

Key words
organise, interpret, data, table, bar chart, title, label, scale

1 **a** Count how many pairs of curtains there are of each colour.
Write the answers in the table.

Colour	Blue	Green	Red	White	Yellow
Number	10				

b Complete the bar chart.

Coloured curtains

SUNM FLATS

2 **a** Which colour is the:
least common?

most common?

b How many flats have yellow curtains?

c How many pairs of curtains are not blue?

Salad	Tuna	Egg	Cheese	Ham

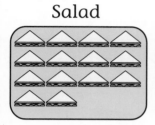 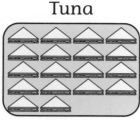 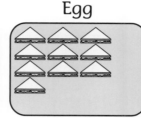 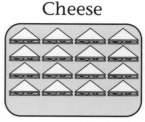 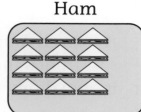

Sandwich	Salad	Tuna	Egg	Cheese	Ham
Number	14				

3 **a** Look at the trays of sandwiches.
Count how many sandwiches of each kind there are.
Write the answers in the table.

b Complete the bar chart.

c How many more tuna sandwiches were there than:

- Salad?
- Cheese?
- Ham?
- Egg?

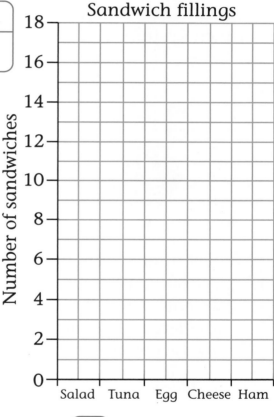

Sandwich fillings

I can show information using tables and bar charts.

Let's try this!

Sanjay asked some students in Year 9 how they liked their eggs cooked.
Use this information to make a table, a bar graph and a pictogram of his data.

Boiled	ЦН |||
Fried	ЦН ЦН ||||
Poached	ЦН ЦН
Scrambled	ЦН ЦН ЦН	

10.5 Using Carroll diagrams

● I can place objects on a Carroll diagram.

Key words
Carroll diagram, sort, classify

A Carroll diagram is used to sort things into sets or groups in two different ways.

This makes it easy to see which objects belong in which group.

	Sides equal	Sides not equal
Has 4 sides		
Does not have 4 sides		

A   B   C   D   E   F   G   H

1 Get a set square for question 1b.
In each Carroll diagram, write the letter of each 2D shape in the correct set.

a

	Has four sides	Does not have four sides
Red	A, D	
Not red		

b

	Yellow	Not yellow
Right angle		
No right angle		

c How many shapes have four sides? ☐

d How many shapes are not yellow and have at least one right angle? ☐

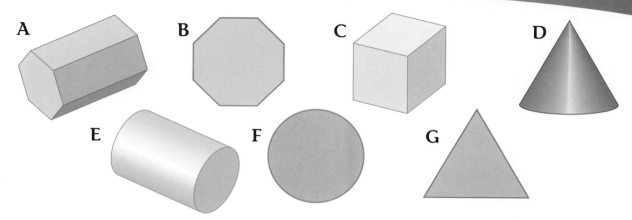

A   B   C   D

E   F   G

2 **a** Write the letter of each shape in the correct set.

	Curved	Not curved
Flat		
Solid		

b How many shapes are curved?

c Which shapes are solids but are not curved.

d Draw a square in the correct set.

I can place objects in a Carroll diagram

Let's try this!

Some sports have been sorted in a Carroll diagram.

Write four sports in the diagram, one for each set.

	Ball	No ball
Net	1 tennis 2	1 ice hockey 2
No net	1 golf 2	1 swimming 2

William Collins's dream of knowledge for all began with the publication of his first book in 1819. A self-educated mill worker, he not only enriched millions of lives, but also founded a flourishing publishing house. Today, staying true to this spirit, Collins books are packed with inspiration, innovation and practical expertise. They place you at the centre of a world of possibility and give you exactly what you need to explore it.

Collins. Freedom to teach.

Published by Collins
An imprint of HarperCollinsPublishers
77–85 Fulham Palace Road
Hammersmith
London
W6 8JB

Browse the complete Collins catalogue at
www.collinseducation.com

ISBN 978-0-00-730286-4

Jeanette Mumford, Simon and Helen Greaves assert their moral right to be identified as the authors of this work.

British Library Cataloguing in Publication Data
A Catalogue record for this publication is available from the British Library.

Commissioned by Priya Govindan
Project managed by Laura Deacon
Literacy review by Cliff Moon
Proof read by Lynn Watkins
Design and typesetting by Steve Evans and Mark Walker Design
Cover design by Julie Martin
Illustrations by Steve Evans and Mark Walker
Production by Therese Theron
Printed and bound by Printing Express, Hong Kong

Answers

CHAPTER 1
NUMBER AND ALGEBRA

1.1 Place value in numbers
1   **b** 27   **c** 71   **d** 84
   e 99   **f** 48   **g** 33
   h 19   **i** 56   **j** 99
2   **b** Sixty-eight   **c** Seventy-seven   **d** Twenty-nine
   e Eighty   **f** Ninety-two   **g** Thirteen
   h Thirty-five   **i** Fifty-one   **j** Forty-six
3   **b** 3 tens   **c** 2 units   **d** 2 tens
   e 0 units   **f** blue shirt and yellow shoe

Let's try this
Various answers possible, for example, choose 4 and 1 to make 41, forty-one, or 14, fourteen.

1.2 Ordering numbers
1   **b** 54   **c** 94   **d** 35   **e** 48   **f** 21
2   **b** 89   **c** 78   **d** 65   **e** 57   **f** 99
3   **b** 48, 53, 56, 69, 70   **c** 57, 72, 75, 87, 88
   d 58, 88, 89, 90, 98

Let's try this
Various answers possible, for example, roll 26, 34, 82, 61, 50 and write in order as 82, 61, 50, 34, 26.

1.3 Odd and even numbers
1   **a** Tick 17, 23, 39 and 25
   b Tick 50, 28, 14 and 42
2   **a** 89, 51, 23, 73, 27, 45, 37
   b 36, 26, 70, 96, 60
3   **b** 16; even   **c** 19; odd   **d** 26, 28; even

Let's try this
Various possible answers, for example, choose 1 and 8 to make 18 which is even or use them to make 81 which is odd.

1.4 Counting in twos, fives and tens
1   **b** 70, 80, 90, 100, 110, 120
   c 35, 40, 45, 50, 55, 60
   d 28, 30, 32, 34, 36, 38
   e 120, 130, 140, 150, 160, 170
   f 65, 70, 75, 80, 85, 90
2   **b** 101   **c** 55   **d** 44
3   **b** 35, 30, 25, 15, 10   **c** 32, 30, 28, 26, 24
   d 5, 9, 11, 13, 15, 17

Let's try this
70, 72, 74, 76, 78, 80, 82, 84, 86, 88
70, 68, 66, 64, 62, 60, 58, 56, 54, 52
70, 75, 80, 85, 90, 95, 100, 105, 110, 115
70, 65, 60, 55, 50, 45, 40, 35, 30, 25

1.5 More sequences
1   **b** 16, 21, 26   **c** 43, 33, 23   **d** 15, 12, 9
2   **a** 26, 31, 36, 41   **b** 18, 22, 26, 30
   c 32, 30, 28, 26   **d** 58, 48, 38, 28
3   **b** 14, 24, 29, 34   **c** 14, 17, 20, 26
   d 50, 45, 40, 35   **e** 32, 28, 24, 20, 16, 12
   f 44, 41, 38, 35, 32   **g** 9, 11, 13, 15, 17, 19

Let's try this
Various possible answers, for example, if the number 22 and the rule + 3 are picked you would make the sequence: 22, 25, 28, 31, 34, 37.

CHAPTER 2
ADDITION AND SUBTRACTION

2.1 Addition and subtraction facts for 100 and 200
1   **b** $90 + 10 = 100$ **c** $50 + 50 = 100$
   d $100 - 30 = 70$ **e** $100 - 40 = 60$
   f $100 - 80 = 20$
2   $11 + 9 = 20$ and $110 + 90 = 200$
   $20 - 4 = 16$ and $200 - 40 = 160$
   $15 + 5 = 20$ and $150 + 50 = 200$
   $20 - 5 = 15$ and $200 - 50 = 150$
   $13 + 7 = 20$ and $130 + 70 = 200$
   $20 - 12 = 8$ and $200 - 120 = 80$
3   **a** 70   **b** 60   **c** 130
   d 80   **e** 40   **f** 150

Let's try this
There are a number of ways to make a total of 100, for example, $70 + 20 + 10$, or $50 + 30 + 20$, or $60 + 40 + 10$.
There are a number of ways to make a total of 200, for example, $90 + 70 + 40$, or $50 + 80 + 70$.

2.2 Subtraction using addition
1   **b** $14 - 9 = 5$; $14 - 5 = 9$ **c** $20 - 8 = 12$; $20 - 12 = 8$
   d $39 - 4 = 35$; $39 - 35 = 4$ **e** $23 - 5 = 18$; $23 - 18 = 5$
   f $49 - 9 = 40$; $49 - 40 = 9$
2   **b** $3 + 5 = 8$; 8   **c** $11 + 9 = 20$; 20
   d $5 + 14 = 19$; 19
3   **b** $8 + 4 = 12$ **c** $14 + 6 = 20$

Let's try this
Various possible answers, for example, choose 5 and 20 and write $5 + 20 = 25$ and $25 - 20 = 5$, $25 - 5 = 20$.

2.3 Adding and subtracting tens
1   **b** 45   **c** 32   **d** 55   **e** 46   **f** 72
   g 69   **h** 63   **i** 27   **j** 68   **k** 47
   l 68
2   **b** 26   **c** 39   **d** 12   **e** 48   **f** 61

3 **b** 24   **c** 67   **d** 28   **e** 95   **f** 38
   g 82   **h** 34   **i** 77   **j** 18   **k** 46
   l 48   **m** 45   **n** 74   **o** 85   **p** 82

Let's try this

Various answers possible, for example, choose 46 and + 30 so write $46 + 30 = 76$, or choose 50 and − 20 so write $50 − 20 = 30$.

2.4 Adding two two-digit numbers

1 **b** $72 + 4 = 76$ **c** $91 + 7 = 98$

   d $53 + 30 + 6 = 83 + 6 = 89$

2 **b** $34 + 50 + 1 = 84 + 1 = 85$

   c $44 + 20 + 5 = 64 + 5 = 69$

   d $63 + 10 + 5 = 73 + 5 = 78$

3 **b** $47 + 20 + 2 = 67 + 2 = 69$

   c $62 + 30 + 7 = 92 + 7 = 99$

   d $85 + 10 + 2 = 95 + 2 = 97$

   e $26 + 40 + 2 = 66 + 2 = 68$

   f $46 + 40 + 3 = 86 + 3 = 89$

Let's try this

Various possible answers, for example, choose 23 and 22 and add to make 55, or 35 and 51 to make 86.

2.5 Subtracting two two-digit numbers

1 **b** $18 − 5 = 13$ **c** $39 − 7 = 32$

   d $55 − 30 − 4 = 25 − 4 = 21$

2 **b** $58 − 20 − 6 = 38 − 6 = 32$

   c $79 − 30 − 5 = 49 − 5 = 44$

   d $94 − 40 − 1 = 54 − 1 = 53$

3 **b** $58 − 30 − 7 = 28 − 7 = 21$

   c $85 − 40 − 2 = 45 − 2 = 43$

   d $99 − 40 − 3 = 59 − 3 = 56$

   e $68 − 20 − 4 = 48 − 4 = 44$

   f $77 − 20 − 2 = 57 − 2 = 55$

Let's try this

Various possible answers, for example, choose 86 and 25 and subtract to make 61, or 69 and 43 to make 26.

CHAPTER 3
TIMES TABLES

3.1 Two and ten times tables

1 **b** 8   **c** 16   **d** 5
   e 10   **f** 7   **g** 6
   h 9

2 **b** $3 × 10 = 30$ **c** $5 × 10 = 50$ **d** $6 × 10 = 60$

3 **a** $5 × 10$ and 50   **b** $7 × 2$ and 14   **c** $10 × 10$ and 100

   d $5 × 2$ and 10   **e** $8 × 10$ and 80   **f** $4 × 2$ and 8

   g $2 × 10$ and 20   **h** $6 × 2$ and 12

Let's try this

Various answers possible, for example, 3 bags of 10 apples to show $3 × 10 = 30$.

3.2 Five times table

1 **b** 20   **c** 45   **d** 3   **e** 10   **f** 7
   g 8   **h** 5   **i** 30   **j** 1

2 **b** $9 × 5 = 45$ **c** $4 × 5 = 20$ **d** $7 × 5 = 35$

3 **b** $10 × 5$ **c** $3 × 5$ **d** $8 × 5$ **e** $7 × 5$

Let's try this

Various answers possible, for example, 3 plates of 5 cakes to show $3 × 5 = 15$.

3.3 Three and four times tables

1   $3 × 4 = 12$ $4 × 4 = 16$ $5 × 4 = 20$
   $6 × 4 = 24$ $7 × 4 = 28$ $8 × 4 = 32$
   $9 × 4 = 36$ $10 × 4 = 40$

2 **a** 9   **b** 20   **c** 30   **d** 24   **e** 5
   f 8   **g** 7   **h** 7

3 **a** $7 × 3 = 21$, $10 × 3 = 30$

   b $8 × 4 = 32$, $9 × 4 = 36$, $6 × 4 = 24$

Let's try this

For example $5 × 4 = 20$, $4 × 5 = 20$, $2 × 10 = 20$, $10 × 2 = 20$ or $3 × 4 = 12$, $4 × 3 = 12$, $6 × 2 = 12$

3.4 Dividing by two, five and ten

1 **b** $12 ÷ 2 = 6$ **c** $10 ÷ 2 = 5$ **d** $16 ÷ 2 = 8$
   e $18 ÷ 2 = 9$ **f** $14 ÷ 2 = 7$ **g** $20 ÷ 2 = 10$
   h $6 ÷ 2 = 3$

2 **a** $5 × 10 = 50$ and $50 ÷ 10 = 5$

   b $4 × 10 = 40$ and $40 ÷ 10 = 4$

   c $9 × 10 = 90$ and $90 ÷ 10 = 9$

   d $7 × 10 = 70$ and $70 ÷ 10 = 7$

3 **a** 2   **b** 4   **c** 5   **d** 6

Let's try this

Various possible answers, for example choose 3 and 10 and write $3 × 10 = 30$ and $30 ÷ 10 = 3$.

3.5 Diving by three and four

1 **b** $21 ÷ 3 = 7$ **c** $18 ÷ 3 = 6$ **d** $28 ÷ 4 = 7$

2 **b** $18 ÷ 3 = 6$ **c** $20 ÷ 4 = 5$ **d** $24 ÷ 3 = 8$
   e $36 ÷ 4 = 9$

3 **b** $15 ÷ 3 = 5$ **c** $12 ÷ 3 = 4$ **d** $20 ÷ 4 = 5$

Let's try this

Various answers possible, for example, draw 20 cakes as 5 boxes of 4 cakes with the division fact $20 ÷ 4 = 5$.

CHAPTER 4
SOLVING PROBLEMS

4.1 Addition problems

2   $50 + 30 = 80$ apples

3   $16 + 4 = 20$ DVDs

4   $8 + 7 = 15$

5   $20 + 30 = 50$ biscuits

6   $12 + 23 = 35$ pizzas

7   $21 + 27 = 48$

Let's try this

Various possible answers for example, Jack has 14 marbles and his friend Jake has 7 marbles. How many marbles do they have altogether?

4.2 Subtraction problems

2 $18 - 7 = 11$ lemon drops

3 $80 - 23 = 57$ pages

4 $98 - 9 = 89$ matches

5 $20 - 11 = 9$ goals

6 $40 - 10 = 30$ strawberries

7 $18 - 12 = 6$ days

8 $35 - 12 = 23$ people

Let's try this

Various possible answers for example, Jack has 50 marbles and he gives 20 of them to his friend Jake. How many marbles does Jack have left?

4.3 Multiplication problems

2 $5 \times 6 = 30$ carrots

3 $8 \times 5 = 40$ slices of pepperoni

4 $4 \times 4 = 16$ chocolate swirls

5 $3 \times 3 = 9$ peppers

6 $7 \times 10 = 70$ doughnuts

7 $7 \times 4 = 28$ onions

8 $3 \times 9 = 27$ bananas

9 $8 \times 3 = 24$ tennis balls

Let's try this

Various possible answers, for example, Daisy buys four boxes of fish-fingers. There are 10 fish-fingers in a box. How many fish-fingers does she buy?

Write the multiplication fact $4 \times 10 = 40$

4.4 Division problems

2 $30 \div 3 = 10$ grapes

3 $100 \div 20 = 5$ hockey sticks

4 $8 \div 4 = 2$ eggs

5 $40 \div 5 = 8$ bracelets

6 $80 \div 10 = 8$ shelves

7 $28 \div 4 = 7$ boxes

Let's try this

$20 \div 2 = 10$ people, $20 \div 5 = 4$ people, $20 \div 4 = 5$ people, $20 \div 10 = 2$ people.

4.5 Money problems

1 **a** 30p **b** 50p **c** 20p
  d 18p

2 **b** $10p + 10p = 20p$ **c** $12p + 7p = 19p$ **d** $12p + 10p = 22p$

3 **b** $50p - 10p = 40p$ **c** $10p - 8p = 2p$ **d** $20p - 16p = 4p$

Let's try this

There are a number of different ways, including these: 10p + 2p, 10p + 1p + 1p, 5p + 5p + 2p, 5p + 2p + 2p + 2p + 1p, 2p + 2p + 2p + 2p + 2p + 2p.

Chapter 5
Fractions

5.1 Halves and quarters

1 **b** $\frac{1}{2}$ **c** $\frac{1}{2}$ **d** $\frac{1}{4}$ **e** $\frac{1}{2}$ **f** $\frac{1}{4}$
  g $\frac{1}{4}$ **h** $\frac{1}{2}$

2 There are a number of different ways to divide each shape in half. Check that the line drawn divides the shape into approximately two equally-sized pieces.

3 There are a number of different ways to divide each shape in quarters. Check that the lines drawn divide the shapes into approximately four equally-sized pieces.

Let's try this

Various answers. Check that the folds divide the shapes into approximately equal-sized parts.

5.2 Fraction of a shape

1 **b** $\frac{1}{5}$ **c** $\frac{1}{5}$ **d** $\frac{1}{3}$

2 **b** Shade any one of the four parts.
  c Shade any one of the five parts.
  d Shade any one of the two parts.

3 **b** $\frac{1}{3}$ **c** $\frac{1}{2}$ **d** $\frac{1}{3}$

4 **a** $\frac{1}{5}$ **b** $\frac{1}{3}$ **c** $\frac{1}{4}$

Let's try this

Various possible answers, for example:

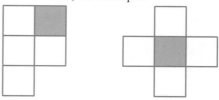

5.3 Fraction of a number

1 **b** 4 paper clips   **c** 6 paper clips   **d** 3 paper clips

2 **a** 2 paper clips   **b** 4 paper clips   **c** 5 paper clips

3 **b** 2 cans   **c** 4 oranges   **d** 3 candles

Let's try this

10 paper clips cannot be shared equally amongst three pots. The following numbers can: 3, 6, 9, 12, 15, 18.....

5.4 More fractions

1 **b** Shade any four of the five parts.
  c Shade any one of the five parts.
  d Shade any three of the five parts.

2 **b** Shade any three of the four parts.
  c Shade any three of the five parts.
  d Shade any two of the four parts.

3 **b** $\frac{1}{2}$ **c** $\frac{2}{3}$

4 **a** $\frac{2}{5}$ **b** $\frac{3}{5}$ **c** $\frac{4}{5}$

Let's try this

$\frac{1}{2}, \frac{1}{3}, \frac{1}{4}, \frac{1}{5}, \frac{2}{3}, \frac{2}{4}, \frac{2}{5}, \frac{3}{4}, \frac{3}{5}, \frac{4}{5}$

5.5 Tenths

1 b Shade any two of the ten parts.

   c Shade any nine of the ten parts.

   d Shade any six of the ten parts.

   e Shade any one of the ten parts.

   f Shade any five of the ten parts.

2 b $\frac{7}{10}$ **c** $\frac{4}{10}$ **d** $\frac{8}{10}$

3 b $\frac{8}{10}$ **c** $\frac{1}{10}$ **d** $\frac{5}{10}$ **e** $\frac{4}{10}$ **f** $\frac{2}{10}$

Let's try this

Various possible answers, for example:

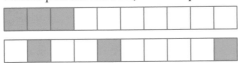

CHAPTER 6
UNDERSTANDING SHAPES

6.1 Naming 2-D shapes

1 a Square   **b** Triangle   **c** Hexagon

   d Pentagon   **e** Hexagon   **f** Triangle

2 a, b, c Students should draw two different five-, six- and eight-sided shapes.

Let's try this!

Students should draw eight different four-sided shapes.

6.2 Compass directions

1 b N   **c** N   **d** E

2 Pyramids – Camel

  Camel   – Tour bus

  Tour bus – Camel

  Obelisk – Tour bus

3 b 3E   **c** 2S   **d** 1W   **e** 3S   **f** 5E

   g 2N

Let's try this!

1

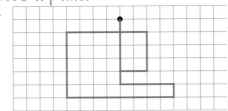

2 Finish back at starting point.

6.3 Using a set square

1 b 2 angles of 90°   e, g, h

   c 4 angles of 90°   a, f

   d No right angles   c, i

2 Square with sides of 6 cm.

3 Answers will vary.

Let's try this!

  a 3 right angles   **b** 5 right angles

6.4 Shape connections

1

Shape	A	B	C	D	E	F
Number of sides	4	8	6	3	5	4
Sides the same length	4	8	6	3	5	4

2
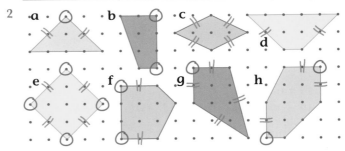

3

Shape	a	b	c	d	e	f	g	h
Number of sides	3	4	4	4	4	5	4	6
Number of equal sides	2	0	4	2	4	2	2	2

Let's try this!

  a e   **b** a   **c** b

6.5 Creating 2-D shapes

1 a   **b**
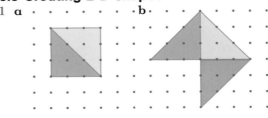

2 a   **b**   **c**   **d**

3
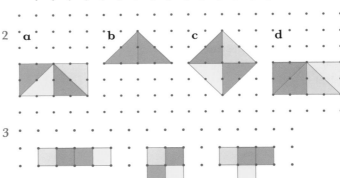

4 See pictures as an example of what students could draw.
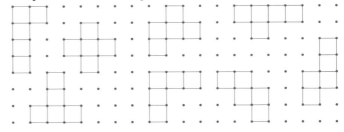

Let's try this!

3 rectangles: 1×12, 2×6 and 3×4

CHAPTER 7
MEASURE – LENGTH AND TIME

7.1 Metres and centimetres

1 b 300 cm   **c** 700 cm   **d** 500 cm   **e** 800 cm

2 1100 cm

3 a

$3\frac{1}{2}$ m = 3 m 50 cm	
$5\frac{1}{2}$ m = 5 m 50 cm	
$2\frac{1}{2}$ m = 2 m 50 cm	
$8\frac{1}{2}$ m = 8 m 50 cm	
$15\frac{1}{2}$ m = 15 m 50 cm	

b

4 m 50 cm = $4\frac{1}{2}$ m
6 m 50 cm = $6\frac{1}{2}$ m
9 m 50 cm = $9\frac{1}{2}$ m
7 m 50 cm = $7\frac{1}{2}$ m
12 m 50 cm = $12\frac{1}{2}$ m

4 a 2m 50 cm = $2\frac{1}{2}$ m = 250 cm

   b $5\frac{1}{2}$ m = 5 m 50 cm = 550 cm

   c 850 cm = 8 m 50 cm = $8\frac{1}{2}$ m

   d 10 m 50 cm = 1050 cm = $10\frac{1}{2}$ m

Let's try this!
Answers will be based on students' findings within the group.

7.2 Measuring to the nearest $\frac{1}{2}$ cm

1 a A = 4 cm, B = 7 cm, C = 9 cm, D = 15 cm

   b $1\frac{1}{2}$ cm, $5\frac{1}{2}$ cm, $9\frac{1}{2}$ cm

   c A – B = 4 cm, B – C = 4 cm, A – C = 8 cm

2 Scorpion = 11 cm, stick insect = 8 cm, kangaroo = 180 cm, flamingo = 90 cm

3 a L = $7\frac{1}{2}$ cm, E = $5\frac{1}{2}$ cm, A = $3\frac{1}{2}$ cm

   b $2\frac{1}{2}$ cm   **c** A   **d** L

Let's try this!
$3 + 4\frac{1}{2} = 7\frac{1}{2}$ m $3 + 6\frac{1}{2} = 9\frac{1}{2}$ m

$4\frac{1}{2}$ m $+ 6\frac{1}{2}$ m = 11 m

7.3 Which standard unit?

1 a m   **b** m   **c** cm   **d** cm   **e** m

   f m   **g** cm

2 a $2\frac{1}{2}$ cm   **b** 10 cm   **c** 20 cm   **d** $\frac{1}{2}$ m

3 A fits 2, B fits 3, C fits 4, D fits 1

Let's try this!
Correct. 8×25 cm = 2 m. Methods will vary.

7.4 Time to the quarter hour

1 b 8 o'clock   **c** $\frac{1}{4}$ past 5   **d** $\frac{1}{4}$ to 4   **e** $\frac{1}{4}$ past 11

   f $\frac{1}{4}$ to 3   **g** $\frac{1}{4}$ past 7   **h** $\frac{1}{4}$ to 9   **i** $\frac{1}{4}$ past 12

2 b 4:15   **c** 12:45   **d** 7:45

3 a 3:00, 3:15, 3:30, 3:45, 4:00, 4:15, 4:30

   b 8:30, 8:45; 9:00, 9:15, 9:30, 9:45, 10:00

Let's try this!
12:15, 12:30, 12:45, 1:00, 1:15, 1:30

7.5 Time to the nearest 5 minutes

1 past: 20, 25   to: 20, 10

2 b 10 to 9   **c** 25 past 12   **d** 5 to 6

   Clock a 5 past 12   **Clock b** 10 to 10

   Clock c 25 past 1   **Clock d** 5 to 7

3 b 8:35   **c** 8:20   **d** 1:50   **e** 6:40   **f** 12:05

   g 12:55   **h** 6:25

4 b 8:35   **c** 3:20   **d** 10:50

Let's try this!
a 3:05, 2:55   **b** 3:30

CHAPTER 8
MEASURE – WEIGHT, CAPACITY AND TIME

8.1 Shopping in grams and kilograms

1 b $4\frac{1}{2}$ kg = 4 kg 500 g = 4500 g

   c 3500 g = 3 kg 500 g = $3\frac{1}{2}$ kg

   d 7 kg 500 g = $7\frac{1}{2}$ kg = 7500 g

   e $9\frac{1}{2}$ kg = 9 kg 500 g = 9500 g

   f 8500 g = 8 kg 500 g = $8\frac{1}{2}$ kg

2

Vegetable bag	Carrots 500 g	Onions 200 g	Pepper 100 g
a	1	2	1
b	1	1	3
c	1	0	5
d	0	4	2
e	0	3	4
f	0	2	6
g	0	1	8

3 a 2800 g   **b** 900 g

Let's try this!
300 g

8.2 Using scales

1 a 700 g   **b** 400 g   **c** 500 g   **d** 900 g   **e** 500 g

   f 300 g   **g** 1100 g   **h** 500 g

2 a about 600 g   **b** about 200 g   **c** about 700 g

3 a 350 g   **b** 250 g   **c** 450 g

Let's try this!
a 200g, 400 g, 800 g

b 250 g, 500 g, 1000 g

8.3 Litres and millilitres

1 b 2500 ml   **c** 4500 ml   **d** 8500 ml

2 a $3\frac{1}{2}l$ **b** $5\frac{1}{2}l$ **c** 6 l **d** $10\frac{1}{2}l$

3 a E   **b** H   **c** I   **d** G

4 b 500 ml   **c** 250 ml   **d** 100 ml

Let's try this!
a 4   **b** 2   **c** 2   **d** 15

8.4 Measuring in millilitres

1 **B** 900 ml   **C** 700 ml   **D** 100 ml

b

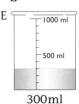 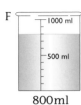 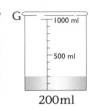 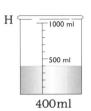

| E 300ml | F 800ml | G 200ml | H 400ml |

    c 700 ml   **d** 200 ml

2 **b** 700 ml   **c** 400 ml   **d** 500 ml

3 **B** 700 ml   **C** 800 ml   **D** 100 ml

Let's try this!

Pot	Amount of paint in ml	Amount of paint in *l*
A	500 ml	$\frac{1}{2} l$
B	750 ml	$\frac{3}{4} l$
C	250 ml	$\frac{1}{4} l$
D	100 ml	$\frac{1}{10} l$

8.5 Measuring time

1 **b** 60 minutes → 1 hour   **c** 7 days → 1 week

   d 24 hours → 1 day   **e** 12 months → 1 year

   f 52 weeks → 1 year   **g** 365 days → 1 year

2 **a** Minutes   **b** Seconds

   c Hours   **d** Seconds

3 **b** 20 min   **c** 10 hours

   d 2 seconds   **e** 7 days

4 There are six possible combinations:

| Sweatshirt | Red | Red | Blue | Blue | Grey | Grey |
| Jeans | Black | Blue | Black | Blue | Black | Blue |

Let's try this!
Answers will vary depending on student's results.

CHAPTER 9
SYMMETRY, POSITION AND MOVEMENT

9.1 Symmetry in 2-D shapes

1

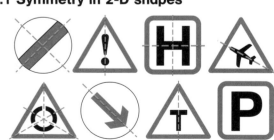

lines of symmetry	Road sign
None	h
One	b, d, f, g
More than one	a, c, e

2 **b** Triangle   **c** Circle   **d** Square   **e** Hexagon
   f Rectangle   **g** Pentagon

Let's try this!
Answers will vary depending on the patterns selected.

9.2 Reflecting shapes

1

   a   **b**   **c**   **d**

  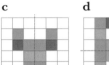

2 **a**   **b**   **c**

     d   **e**

Let's try this!
Examples could be as follows.

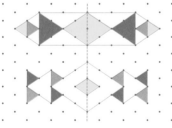

9.3 Find your position

1 **a** Beta rig   **b** Delta rig   **c** E1   **d** B5

   e D2   **f** A2

2 **a** B1   **b** A2   **c** C3   **d** A4

   e A1   **f** C4   **g** B2   **h** B3

3 **a** Sam   **b** Rob

Let's try this!
Open

9.4 Describing 3-D solids

1 **ab** Rectangular prisms – orange; square prisms – green; triangular prisms – blue; hexagonal prisms - red

2 **A** ✔   **B** ✘   **C** ✔   **D** ✘

   E ✔   **F** ✔   **G** ✘   **H** ✘

3 a A has 6 faces   **b** B has 3 faces   **c** E has 8 faces
   d F has 12 edges   **e** D has 0 edges   **f** H has 0 edges

Let's try this!

3-D solid	Number of faces	Number of edges of an end face
Cube	6	4
Cuboid	6	4
Triangular prism	5	3
Hexagonal prism	8	6

9.5 Faces of 3-D shapes

1

3-D shape \ 2-D faces	Circle	Triangle	Square	Rectangle	Pentagon	Hexagon
a Cuboid			2	4		
b Triangular prism		2		3		
c Cylinder	2			1		
d Cube			6			
e Hexagonal prism				6		2
f Pentagonal prism				5	2	

2 b Cuboid   **c** Triangular prism
   d Square-based pyramid   **e** Cube   **f** Cone

Let's try this!

Prism end face	Number of sides of end face	Number of faces
Triangle	3	5
Square	4	6
Pentagon	5	7
Hexagon	6	8
Octagon	8	10

Prediction: prism with an end face of 7 sides has 9 faces.

CHAPTER 10
HANDLING DATA

10.1 Tally charts

1 a Totals:

Car – 26, Bus – 18, Motorbike – 9, Lorry/van – 14,
Bicycle – 10

b

Transport	Tally	Frequency
Car	卌 卌 卌 卌 卌 l	26
Bus	卌 卌 卌 lll	18
Motorbike	卌 llll	9
Lorry/van	卌 卌 llll	14
Bicycle	卌 卌	10

c 8   **d** 19

2 a Frequencies – Supermarket = 13, Corner shop = 7,
market stall = 11, greengrocer = 4

b supermarket
c 7   **d** 35

3 a

Bread	Tally	Frequency
White	卌 卌 卌 ll	17
Brown	卌 卌 卌 卌	20
Crusty	卌 卌 l	11
Pitta	卌 lll	8
Naan	llll	4

b brown   **c** 20   **d** 6

Let's try this!

The volume of transport passing the school at 6 am would be
considerably less. The frequencies for the types of transport at 6
am would probably be less than half of those at lunchtime.

10.2 Using pictograms

1 a

Day	Frequency
Sunday	11
Monday	6
Tuesday	4
Wednesday	3
Thursday	8
Friday	6
Saturday	12

b Wednesday   **c** Saturday, Sunday
d Monday, Friday   **e** 50

2 a

Coin	Number
1p	17
2p	14
5p	19
10p	7
20p	10

b

Coins collected for 'Children in Need'

Key: ◯ = 2 coins

c most common: 5p, least common: 10p

Let's try this!

Coins collected for 'Children in Need'

Key: ◯ = 2 coins

10.3 Block graphs

1 a

Can	Number
Cherry	5
Cola	7
Lemonade	2
Orange	10

b Cans of drink

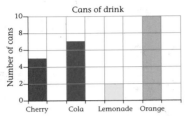

2

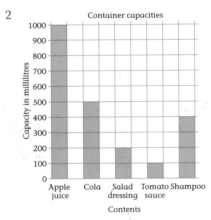

3 a Tomato sauce   **b** Shampoo   **c** Salad dressing

Let's try this!
Open

10.4   Bar charts

1 a

Colour	Blue	Green	Red	White	Yellow
Number	10	6	5	6	7

b

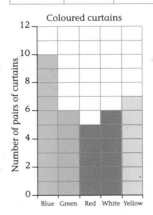

2 Least common = red; most common = blue

   b 7   **c** 24

3 a

Sandwich	Salad	Tuna	Egg	Cheese	Ham
Number	14	18	10	16	12

b

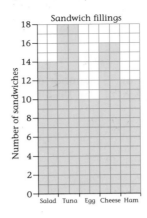

c Salad: 4, Cheese: 2, Ham: 6, Egg: 8

Let's try this!
Table

Type of egg	Boiled	Fried	Poached	Scrambled
Number	8	14	10	16

Bar graph

Pictogram

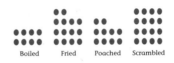

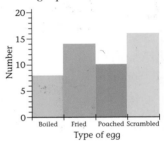

10.5 Using Carroll diagrams

1 a

	Has 4 sides	Does not have 4 sides
Red	A, D, H	F
Not red	E	B, C, G

b

	Yellow	Not yellow
Right angle	C, G	A, D, E, F
No right angle		B, H

c 4   **d** 4

2 a

	Curved	Not curved
Flat	F	B, G
Solid	D, E	A, C

b 3   **c** A: hexagonal prism, C: cube

d In set: flat / not curved

Let's try this!
Examples include:
(Net, ball) = Netball
(No net, ball) = Squash
(Net, no ball) = Badminton
(No net, no ball) = Athletics